ZONE SYSTEM MANUAL

PREVISUALIZATION

EXPOSURE

DEVELOPMENT

PRINTING

by Minor White

The Ansel Adams Zone System as a Basis
of Intuitive Photography

MORGAN & MORGAN, INC. PUBLISHERS

Dobbs Ferry, N.Y. 10522

First Printing 1967
Second Printing 1968
Third Printing 1970
Fourth Printing 1972
Fifth Printing 1994

The idea of previsualization is merely wonderful.
The Practice of previsualization is the master key
to expressive-creative photography and Camerawork.

Minor White

COPYRIGHT © 1968 – MINOR WHITE
MORGAN & MORGAN, INC., DOBBS FERRY, N.Y. 10522

Library of Congress Catalog Card No. 61-12640

Printed by Morgan Press Incorporated, Dobbs Ferry, N.Y.

TABLE OF CONTENTS

B

A

C

Figure 1. THE FIRST DEMONSTRATION: VISUAL MEASUREMENT IN ZONES.
Each of the three photographs reproduced (left) was made from its own negative. To produce these special negatives three sheets of film were exposed in one "stop" increments, for example f/6 at 1/100, 1/50, 1/25, respectively from darkest to lightest.

After the printing time of one negative was adjusted to give a literal rendering of the scene, A, this same exact printing time was given to the other negatives.

All the values in C are said to be one zone lighter than the values in A. The values in corresponding areas in B are all said to be one zone darker than seen in A.

ONE ZONE DIFFERENCE IN EXPOSURE AND CORRESPONDING CHANGE IN PRINT VALUE IS THE BASIS UPON WHICH ZONE AS AN EYE-VISUAL MEASUREMENT RESTS.

Since *all* the values from darkest to lightest changed characteristically, it is possible to see in these prints how an exposure change of one stop or one zone affects the entire print scale.

How a print value scale looks when the various zones are arranged sequentially may be seen in Figure 2, column B, page 14.

Previsualization, and a Zone System

This manual is for those who learn by doing. To try to understand previsualization merely by reading is hopeless. Hence demonstrations are outlined, which if done, will bring the photographer to previsualization by *experience*. Once the idea has been suffused by practice through the whole man, previsualization will be understood in the right way.

The zone system long associated with Ansel Adams is one of many means of learning to previsualize. It is the one possibly best fitted to the medium of photography, professional and amateur. The serious photographer will find in the zone system a direct, workable way of always getting the most out of his films, papers, and chemicals. The amateur who realizes that he is the victim of his equipment and materials can discover in the zone system a positive means of mastering his medium. The professional will find the system so flexible that he can gain a use of any and all of the materials that he wants to use: roll film, black and white, color, Polaroid, etc.

PREVISUALIZATION IS FOR THOSE WHO WANT MORE.

Hence, this manual is for those who want more out of photography than is popularly practiced; those who want to explore and extend their expressive-creative ability. Alfred Stieglitz, at the beginning of the century called the expressive use of the medium, "Camerawork." Edward Weston recognized it as "the flame of recognition," or the "moment of revelation." Henri Cartier-Bresson refers to it as "The Decisive Moment."

Previsualization in practice can lead the photographer to work freely in any mode of the expressive-creative: the literal as well as the non-literal, the Document as well as the Equivalent, the Pictorial as well as the Promotional, with informative as well as stimulating images. Quite simply, previsualization is the key to the creative and expressive use of the medium on a conscious level.

To be able to previsualize takes a little talent. Certainly those photographers who can see through surfaces to the truths within can learn to previsualize freely and spontaneously. The Zone System among its other attributes, helps to make certain that one's ability to previsualize, after practice, achieves spontaneity.

In a book — no, but in *practice*, to previsualize is to be led towards the essential resonances in photography: the resonances between subject and photographer at the time of exposure; the resonance between him and his print later; and finally the essential resonance between photographer and audience.

The ultimate objective is to be able to previsualize as one wishes, spontaneously or leisurely whichever best serves the purposes at hand. There is a difference in the penetrating power of an image made in a burst of naive enthusiasm and those made in a flash of *trained* intuition. The first is adolescent, the latter mature and sometimes wise.

This new edition reflects much of what has been learned in twenty years of offering previsualization by a Zone System in academic classes and private workshops. A chapter has been added on how to read in zones most of today's luminance meters. A more lucid testing procedure is included. And anyone who has made his own prints can do the demonstration found in Chapter 1, where the challenge of the Zone System first appears.

Today's printing papers seem to be designed mainly for the commercial photographer; they tend to compress the black end of the scale, and block the white end. For this reason we have reduced the basic gray scale used for previsualization from 10 steps to 9. Consequently in this edition Zone Zero has been eliminated, Zone I has been redefined as maximum photographic black, and Zone II as the first printable separation of tone (with a density in negatives as 0.13 over film base plus fog.) Zone VII is redefined as textured White instead of Zone VIII.

While the newer papers are hard to print on, that does not destroy the act or the practice of previsualization. Contrary to popular myth, previsualization is done according to whatever film and paper will actually be exposed.

To many individuals I extend a profusion of gratitude. My students have taught me all I know about the subject. Ansel Adams has been more than generous in helping me to prepare this guide to planned photography, the fullness of which may be found in his Basic Photo Series. I have untold gratitude to Willard D. Morgan who has kept the Zone System in print since 1946. I have many thanks for John L. Davenport who first stated the concept of subject contrast control by variable film development in two articles in *U.S. Camera*, 1934.

Minor White

7

1. The First Demonstration

Visual Measurement in Zones

Among the many contributions made to photography by Ansel Adams is the name "Zone" for what in effect is a visual measurement based on the 1:2 exposure ratio universally used in photography. Because a "Zone" is not a single shade of grey, the Adams concept of the zone in photography provides an elastic rather than a rigid measurement. Elasticity is just what the unaided eye needs in order to "see like a camera". And to see photographically in a spontaneous and conscious manner.

To get a fast look at this practical visual measurement called "Zone", and a glimpse at the system that develops out of the concept, make 3 photographs for comparison as follows. Figure 1 is a sample.

First locate a scene the middle values (or tones, or shades of grey) of which occupy about one half the future picture area, the dark values or shadows about a quarter, and the light values the rest. A scene should be chosen that is full of big plain surfaces so that the comparisons of identical areas later in the various prints will be easy. The size of the areas in Figure 1 is a fair example.

The pictures for comparison may be made with conventional B & W, color transparencies, or any of the Polaroid cameras that will allow changes of exposure by one or more stops. Polaroid is the simplest and quickest if one has the equipment; color requires two projectors in order to compare images. In the long run black and white, either sheet or roll, may be the most satisfactory for this demonstration.

1. EXPOSURE.   Make 3 identically framed pictures of the same scene. The first is to be exposed for an "average" or "realistic" rendering; the second to be exposed for one half the time of the first, or one "stop" less exposure. The third is to be given twice the exposure of the first.

2. PRINTING.   Assuming that the development time of all three negatives is identical, adjust the printing time of the first negative until a "realistic" or literal print is obtained. Print on a #2 projection paper. Figure 1.

Print the other two negatives at *exactly* the same time, same #2 paper contrast, same print development so that the unadulterated effect of changing exposure one stop for each successive negative is clearly visible. (Printing one negative at three successive stops on the enlarger will not give quite the same results.)

3. COMPARISON OF PRINTS: 1. *The Middle Values*

For the starting comparison, one of the middle grey areas is chosen. (Comparisons in shadow and light areas are made later.) See Figure 1 at D.

Compare a middle grey area in the print from the first negative with the corresponding area in the print of the second negative: this is the darkest print. Cutting or folding the second print through the area being compared will help the eye see the difference in the two values without interference.

The difference in values between the two selected areas is said to be one zone.

Next compare the same area with the corresponding area in the third print. The difference in values is again said to be one zone. In this case it is one zone lighter. Memorize these differences. The difference is the basic visual measurement used for previsualization in photography.

4. COMPARISON OF PRINTS WITH ORIGINAL SCENE

Take the prints back to the original subject. If all of them are trimmed or folded through the area used for comparison, the eye will be able to see the various differences accurately.

Providing that one has been lucky, the area under consideration found in the first or "realistic" print will match or

9

almost match the value of the corresponding area in the original subject. If not, then perhaps one of the other prints will: a close match is sufficient for this particular demonstration.

Assuming here, in this manual, that one of the prints matches the original value, the rest of the prints clearly demonstrate that the camera can render or record a middle grey value in the original so that (1) it matches the original, or (2) it is darker than the original, or (3) it is lighter. And in measurable differences that the unaided eye can remember.

If no mistakes were made in preparing the negatives and prints for this demonstration, and they are arranged progressively dark to light, each negative differs by one stop, and each print is darker or lighter by one zone.

These three innocent looking prints imply much.

5. IMPLICATIONS OF THE 3 PRINTS: *Previsualization*

The three prints show that a value in a scene that the eye sees as a constant, the camera can record variously. The reason being that the eye transmits, or passes light through itself, whereas the photographic emulsions "collect" light.

If his medium "sees" in this peculiar way, then man can learn to cope with such seeing. He has will and imagination, at least a little, and while he can not alter the physical nature of his eyes to "store" light as photographic emulsions do, he is able to train his imagination to visualize the effects of such storage. Since this operation is generally done by users of the zone system before actual exposure is made, the process of imagining values in potential prints while staring at values in a scene is called Previsualization.

In these three innocent looking prints we are presented with the challenge that the word "Previsualization" stands for in photography. That is, to superimpose an imagined image in the mind onto an image held in the eye-brain.

To do this requires an effort . . . the kind of an effort long associated with creativity.

In other words standing in front of the scene with prints in hand, one can try to mentally impose a lighter or darker version of the scene while looking at it directly. Reference to the actual prints from time to time will help.

6. COMPARISON OF PRINTS: 2. *High and Low Values*

Up to this point we have worked exclusively with a value in the middle of what is called a print value scale, or a print grey scale. Now we can consider the light and dark ends of this same print value scale.

The difference between zones in the light and dark ends of the value scale are quite subtle. When the reader has done the practical work up to this stage his ability to distinguish zones will be sufficiently improved that he will have no trouble working with still closer differences.

Every single area in print #2, for example, will be one zone different than its corresponding area in print #3, and so on. Therefore one can look at the difference in values between two identical dark areas and see the exact differences of one zone there. The same holds true for the light areas. What must be closely observed is that one zone differences in both the dark and light areas will be *less than* the difference found in the middle values. This is typical and characteristic of photographic emulsion renderings.

7. PHOTOGRAPHIC VALUE SCALE

The various values from black to white which are scattered helter skelter in a print may be reorganized into a simple progression from black to white. Such a print value scale is shown in Figure 3, where it is called a "value ruler" because it can be moved about over prints to check zone renderings. Figures 4 and 6 show how such print value scales may be attached to two types of luminance meters.

8. Comparison With The Original Scene Again

Return with the prints to the original scene. Start by holding up the print that was found to match the middle grey area. When the middle grey value matches the original area, notice that most of the higher and lower values do *not* match their corresponding areas. This is also typical of photographic rendering.

Only a moment's thought will make us realize that in every exposure we make, even when we plan a literal rendering, some values will not be accurately rendered, that is, will not match. Consequently in every exposure that we make an opportunity is presented to us, if we choose to take it, to previsualize some of the values as lighter or darker than what our eye reports.

As was said, previsualization is made possible by an effort of imagination. As was also said, such effort partakes somehow in what we commonly call creativity.

PREVISUALIZATION WiTH MATERIALS LIMITED TO EXPOSURE CHANGES

In this first demonstration directions were given by which we could isolate the changes in rendering caused by changing exposure alone. Later, in Chapter 4, directions are given by which can be seen the effect on rendering caused by altering development time of the film.

Many films such as Polaroid or color transparencies, sent to a processing lab, confine the photographer's picture rendering control mainly to exposure. That is, a change in exposure causes a corresponding change in rendering. In these films the development time is necessarily restricted to an optimum. Though the restricted development control limits the possibilities of the *material,* this does not hinder previsualization. *Previsualization, as was said, is always done according to the nature of the film in the camera and the photographic printing paper in the dark room.*

2. Preliminary Definitions

Orientation to the interrelations between Previsualization, Luminance Meters and a Zone System starts with a few definitions. To arrive at fuller definitions, the reader should perform the various demonstrations in the manual. After such experience he will have definitions that are especially fitted to himself.

PREVISUALIZATION

Previsualization stands for the act of looking at a scene with the physical eye and seeing in the mind's eye how a medium can render the subject.

Previsualization refers to the learnable power to look at a scene, person, place or situation and "see" at the same time on the back of the eyelids, or "sense" deep in the mind or body, the various ways photography can render the subject. Then out of all the potential renderings select one to photograph. Such selection makes up a large share of the photographer's creativity.

For example, anyone can look at a yellow house, the yellow color of which he does not like. Since he dislikes yellow he can previsualize the house in his favorite color, say purple. To actualize his wish he has only to paint the house purple, or make a drawing in purple crayon or an oil in purple paint. To make a corresponding color change in a photographic rendering is impossible in Black & White, and difficult in color printing. The medium of photography, as do all media, has limitations. *Hence the actual light-sensitive material in the camera and how this will be processed and printed is always taken into account as the basis of photographic previsualization.* No matter what

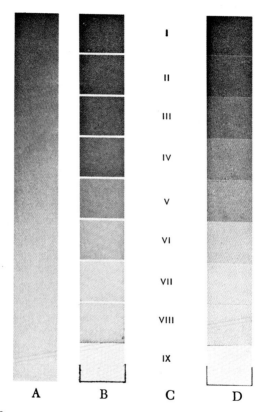

Figure 2

Tones or values of grey are fundamental to the medium of photography. This central element is displayed above, in the form of "grey scales." At A is seen a "continuous-value" grey scale. At B this is separated into segments, each segment of which exhibits continuous-tone. At C these "zones" are keyed with Roman numerals. At D notice that each segment is but a *single* shade of grey which symbolizes all the greys of its zone.

kind of film or light-sensitive printing paper, to previsualize as one chooses one has only to learn the nature of the materials whether that be roll film, sheet film, Color, Black & White, Polaroid, prints, transparencies or whatever will be invented in years to come.

Previsualization may be developed to the speed and intensity called intuitive.

ZONE

A "Zone" as a visual unit of measurement is arrived at by altering a standard exposure by one "stop" more or one "stop" less. For example all the values in a scene exposed at f/11 at 1/25 second would print one "zone" lighter than a print of the same scene exposed at f/16 at 1/25 second. (Providing of course that the two negatives were given identical development time and the same exposure time in the enlarger.)

This "one Stop" or "one Zone" alteration, links the "zone" to the classic 1:2 exposure ratio used in photography to calibrate shutter speeds and diaphragm openings or "stops."

In a comparison of two prints made of the same subject, one made at twice the exposure of the other, the difference between the values seen in identical areas is said to be a *one zone difference.* For the purpose of previsualization this difference is memorized. While the eye can match two values almost exactly when seen side by side or only slightly separated, even the trained mind previsualizes best within the tolerance of a zone.

LUMINANCE METERS

As previsualization needs a concept, so the Zone System needs a tool, the luminance meter.

Luminance meters useful for previsualization measure light reflected from surfaces and carry various scales by which exposures are "indicated."

The Zone System embodies the concept of the 1:2 exposure ratio by which most luminance meters can be read

I

II

III

IV

V

VI

VII

VIII

IX

The value scale at the left may be used as if it were a "ruler." If this "value ruler" were cut out and then moved about the print image at the right, all the Zones from I to VIII could be matched. (White is missing because half tone reproduction does not include white.)

Figure 3

A "VALUE RULER" AND THE NORMAL PRINT

The Normal Print is uniquely photographic and defined as one with all of its full scale of values showing and a sense of substance everywhere. The shadows are open, the highlights textured, and the middle values luminous. It provokes a sense of visual "realism," of faithfulness to surfaces and substances, as space, air and the sense of light.

The Normal Print is first an ideal, and second a point of departure from which all derivations and stylizations and interpretations may be previsualized, planned and actualized.

in "zones." Once conceptualized, the luminance meters may be used to manipulate these three factors: exposure, development, and the contrast grades of photographic printing paper. The luminance meter is *in effect* a tool for the control of value rendering. *Hence the luminance meter functions as the center of the interrelations between light, subject, previsualization, camera, materials, photographer's purposes, print and future audience.*

VALUE SCALE

The term "value" is used in the language of the zone system about as it is in science and art. The term "value" refers to the degree of lightness and darkness of a color, whereas "hue" refers to the, for example, "greeness" of the green.

In a photographic print the display of greys or values is known as the "scale." The *characteristic* photographic grey scale is said to be "continuous." That is, the medium is capable of rendering such subtle changes from grey to grey that the eye can not discern even faint steps between. This "continuous scale" is illustrated in column A in Figure 2.

To aid previsualization the continuous value scale is arbitrarily divided into 9 steps. This is seen in column B in Figure 2. For still greater convenience in notations a single specific value is taken to represent all the values of *each* zone. This is seen in column D in Figure 2.

VALUE RENDERING

The term "rendering" is used rather than "recording" because few photographs are more than gross approximations of the actual values found in the originals. The fact that photographs are considered "realistic" is a tribute to the eagerness of human beings to attribute realism to the literal. The term "rendering" also suggests that there may be choice among possibilities of interpretations, the number of interpretations being limited by the medium.

With the above definitions it may be stated that the technical problem of photography is to render subject values as print values. In the Zone System value rendering is planned and previsualized in zones.

ZONE SYSTEM

The Zone System rests on the fact that it is both practical and spiritual to be a conscious photographer.

With the concepts of Zones photographers may previsualize in visual units of measurement. In addition these visual units make it possible for photographers to (1) "translate" subject values into print values, (2) work out favorable solutions to the ever present problem of making a photographic interpretation of a real object in terms of exposure, develement and printing, (3) in darkroom and viewing place complete image plans made *before* exposure.

PLACE, FALL & DEVELOP TO

In practice subject values are "translated" into print values by means of the luminance meter. The term *Place* is used in conjunction with exposure determination. The term *Fall* relates to development determination. The term *Develop to* also relates to development determinations and their implementation.

NORMAL PRINT

The uniquely photographic print is taken as the standard for previsualization. This means shadow glowing with detail and white, truthful with texture. The Normal print serves both as an ideal and as a point of departure for all possible derivations. **Figure 3.**

The Normal Print is one made from a film that was exposed to a Normal contrast range, i.e. 9 consecutive luminance values and developed Normally, i.e. the least number of minutes any specific film in its companion developer, the resultant negatives of which, when printed by time and temperature, on medium (No. 2) contrast grade of photographic paper, will reproduce 9 consecutive *Luminance Values as the 9 Print Zones.*

3. Previsualization And The Luminance Meter

READING LUMINANCE METERS IN ZONES

The ideal luminance meter to help previsualization would have two scales. One scale for the measurement of luminance, and numbered. The other, to *visually* represent the print value scale with Zones of grey.

Of contemporary meters (1967) only Weston's Ranger 9 has a visual print value scale. Honeywell's Pentax 3/21 and Mekano's Spotron have dials that allow easy attachment of a visual Zone value scale.

Figure 4

The Weston Master III has one of the easiest to read of all the various dials in later models.

A Print Zone scale attached to the meter dial makes visible the relation of *Print Values* to the "grey scale" of the meter. Observe that the grey tone of each Print Zone extends one "block" on either side of the Light Value number. Remember that the single tone and the corresponding Roman numeral is but a symbol for a "short series of adjacent greys" or zone.

(Lower right) Supplementary dial available from Weston Instrument Corporation for the Ranger 9 Weston Exposure Meter. Note that the Zone Value Scale is incorporated in the dial system.

Luminance meters other than the Westons and Honeywells are so designed that it is difficult to attach print value scales. Consequently these other meters require numerical manipulations to read them in zones. With a little extra effort the manipulations are workable, and with practice implement previsualization very well.

In this chapter on luminance meters the sections on reading exposure and reading development are divided into *Weston & Honeywell* types and *Others*. The others are represented by Leica meters, General Electric, Lunasix and so on. (The meters coupled to automated cameras are designed to *prevent* manipulation and so offer no help in reading development indications).

ARROWS & ZONE V.

To read luminance meters in zones and especially to read indicated development, two primary facts must be known and remembered. First, of all the various arrows, pointers, blocks, red dots and so on are "averaging devices". Second, the *exposure indicating systems* of most luminance meters are *based on a middle grey* or a Zone V.

1. "Averaging devices." The averaging devices are logical for careless use of luminance meters because the majority of scenes and subjects present an "average" contrast. The various devices which average the high and low readings of a scene, or the difference between the darkest and lightest part of a scene will give an exposure indication that will be "good enough" most of the time. For previsualization, however, and for reading exposure and *development* from luminance meters it is necessary to be able to measure, somehow, the differences between the darkest and lightest values of a subject that are to be included in a rendering. (On this account Incident Light Meters are useless for previsualization, because they are unable to measure the contrast of the scene to be photographed.)

2. *"Exposure Systems based on Zone V."* The fact that

luminance meters in general, including the Weston and the Honeywell are calibrated to a middle grey, or an 18% reflectance, means just this: that the indicated exposure for any *one* subject value, if actually given, will render *that* subject value in Zone V in the print.

Since this second fact comes as a surprise to many persons an illustration is in order.

Consider a large screen evenly illuminated and painted in three wide bands, dark, light and middle grey. Any luminance would indicate a different exposure for each band. If the indicated exposures were actually given and three separate negatives were made, *each negative would have the same density*. And each print would display a Zone V.

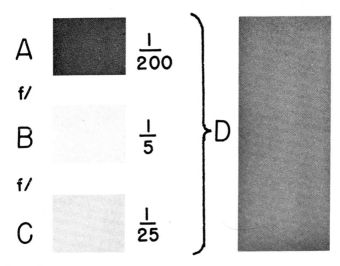

Figure 5
LUMINANCE METER EXPOSURE INDICATIONS ARE BASED ON ZONE V.
The secret of reading luminance meters in zones depends on the fact that the majority of luminance meters average the light reaching their light sensitive cells, and that the various *exposure indications* are calibrated to yield a middle grey value of about 18% reflectance. This means in practice that if each of the three bands above, A, B, & C were exposed to separate sheets or frames of film according to the indicated exposures, each individual band would be rendered as a Zone V value as seen at D.

EXPOSURE DETERMINATIONS
with Weston and Honeywell Luminance Meters

The terms *place,* or *placement* are used to help determine exposure. *Placement* is accomplished when a specific luminance reading number on the "Light Level" is rotated to be opposite a *selected* Zone on the Print Value Scale. In Figure 6 a luminance reading of 10 in a shadow area is shown as *placed* opposite a Zone III on both meters. Zone III was selected because that would give the minimum exposure required to render detail in the shadow. So placed any combination of aperture and shutter speed indicates identical exposure.

Exposure determinations in zones follow the old rule of thumb, "*Expose for the shadows,* and develop for the highlights." In the Zone System "shadow" is defined as the darkest area in a scene or subject in which one *intends* to render detail. *This need not be the darkest part of the scene that the eye can register.* The luminance reading of this "shadow" is placed in Zone III by rotating the dials as explained above.

HOW SUBJECT VALUES ARE PREVISUALIZED AS PRINT VALUES

The translation of subject values into print values is controlled by rotating movable dials so that specific readings on the light value or "light level" dials come opposite *selected* zones on the print zone dial. In the meters illustrated, Figure 6A and B, especially prepared *print zone value scales* are pasted on. Thus that particular part of the meters which is directly related to print values and print zones is made instantly visible.

In the two meters illustrated a reading of 11 on a face in shadow was obtained by both. The dials of each were swung so that the 11 is opposite Zone IV in each case. In the Zone System meters are so calibrated to the light sensitive material that an 11 opposite a IV means that the face in shadow will be rendered in some specific value within the limits of the various Zone IV values.

Once a luminance reading of a meter is placed opposite a Zone on that meter, the dials which carry the aperture and shutter speed numbers fall into various combinations which indicate exposure. Any one of the various combinations would let as much light reach the film as any other combination. Of all the combinations offered one chooses which pair according to whether one wishes to stop action or control the depth of field. To stop action some combination such as 1/500 second at f/4.5 would be chosen. If considerable depth of field was required the 1/10 second at f/32 would be selected.

Figure 6A

The Weston Master V with a specially made *print value scale* pasted on. It was pasted on so that Zone V covers the famous arrow, hence the latter is out of sight. The dials have been arbitrarily swung so that number 12 is opposite Zone V. Zone I is seen opposite the number 8, and Zone VIII is opposite the number 15. On this meter the print zone dial rotates.

Figure 6B

The Honeywell Pentax showing how a *print zone value scale* is wrapped around the tube. The Zone V is pasted over the red dot on the tube. In this case the dot and the V are seen opposite number 12. On this meter the light value ring rotates. Use the Mekano Spotron meter in the same way.

EXPOSURE DETERMINATIONS
with Other Types of Luminance Meters

With most luminance meters, other than the Weston and Honeywell, *placement* in zones is accomplished by manipulating *the indicated exposures* in a prescribed way.

The procedure is this. A reading of the "shadow" area is taken. This "shadow" area is planned for a Zone III rendering. Since the indicated exposure *if actually* given would render the "shadow" area in Zone V, as we saw in Figure 5, some other exposure is necessary. The exposure required to render the area in Zone III is two "stops" or two zones *less* than indicated. For example, a luminance reading of 7 on a *General Electric* is obtained for a "shadow" reading. The indicated exposure is $f/11$ at 1/10 second. (These figures are arbitrary.) If given, the "shadow" would be rendered in Zone V. If an actual exposure of $f/11$ at 1/25 second were given, or one zone *less* exposure, the area would be rendered in Zone IV. If an exposure of $f/11$ at 1/50 second were given, i.e. two zones less exposure, were actually given, the area would be rendered in Zone III, the rendering planned and wanted.[°]

To make the procedure a little more visible a chart is presented.

In the diagram below the Roman numerals stand for Zones on a print value scale and the fractions represent shutter speeds. The aperture is assumed to be identical for all indicated exposures in the diagram, in this case it could be f/11.

I	II	III	IV	V	VI		VII	VIII	IX
				1/10			A	Indicated exposure	
			1/25				B	one zone less	
		1/50					C	two zones less	

[°] **Placement** with the majority of meters, is more a matter of placing a **rendering** than placing a luminance value. Fortunately, value rendering in prints may be previsualized with any meter regardless of semantics.

A. The indicated exposure would render the "shadow" area in Zone V.

B. 1/25 second, if given, would render the "shadow" area in Zone IV.

C. 1/50 second, if given, would render the "shadow" area in Zone III.

The chart is both visible and basic and in an *extended form* is used for determining both exposure *and* development with the majority of meters. This is explained in the section on pages 29 and 30.

DETERMINATIONS OF DEVELOPMENT
with Honeywell and Weston Meters

The terms *Fall* and *Develop to* are employed in Zone System language in relation to the determinations of film development indications.

After one luminance reading is *placed* (and thereby setting an indicated exposure) all other luminance readings of that subject are said to *Fall*. For example the reading of the shadow side of a face read 10. This placement of 10 opposite Zone III is shown on the Weston meter in Figure 6A, and on the Honeywell in 6B. On both meters the luminance reading 11 then *Falls* on Zone IV; the 13 *Falls* opposite (or "in") Zone VI and so on for all the other readings of the subject contrast.

The distinction between *place* and *fall* is significant to the previsualizer. The distinction is important because it helps him remember that the relative difference between values in the subject *remain the same* in the print. For example that which is one zone, two zones, five zones brighter, or conversely whatever number of zones darker, exhibit the same *relationship* in the print. (Only with filters and subjects of intense and brilliant colors is it possible to "reverse" subject values in a print.)

After the "shadow" value is placed in Zone III wherever the luminance reading of the *brightest part* of the subject *falls* is some kind of a measurement of the contrast range of the subject. By classifying subject contrast ranges by zones "development indications" may easily be read in zones.

With Weston meters and a Zone III placement *Zone VII* is taken as the upper limit for development indications. This is because the 30 degree angle covered by the light gathering cell does not permit accurate readings and so the *actual* number of zones included in a III to VII measurable subject contrast range is about 9 zones. The Zone III placement actually includes Zones II - I - and Zero, although they can not be read at all. Likewise at the bright end the Zone VII reading generally includes Zones VIII and IX thereby assuring texture.

After a Zone III placement of the "shadow" luminance reading of the subject, if the highest reading falls in *Zone VII*, "the development indication" is said to be Normal.

If the highlight reading *falls* in Zone VIII, the Development indication is Normal minus one Zone — symbolized as N—1. This means that the development time of the film would be decreased "one zone's worth" that is, just enough less development so that a subject value which with Normal development *would be* rendered in Zone VIII, will actually print in *Zone VII*.

If the highlight reading were to fall in Zone VI the development indication is Normal plus one zone, or N+1. Or in Zone System language the area exposed to Zone VI would be *developed to* Zone VII.

You are strongly advised to look at what these wide angle meters actually include for every reading.

A rule of thumb chart of these *Indicated developments* will consolidate this information for wide angle luminance meters such as the Weston.

"DEVELOPMENT INDICATIONS" FOR WIDE ANGLE LUMINANCE METERS (WESTON)

Table 1.

"Shadow" Placed	High Value Falls	Indicated Development	to render "textured" white area in
III	X	N—3	VII
"	IX	N—2	"
"	VIII	N—1	"
"	VII	Normal	"
"	VI	N+1	"
"	V	N+2	"
"	IV	N+3	"

With *narrow angle* luminance meters such as the Honeywell, with a Zone III placement, the upper limit may be standardized on Zone VIII. So a rule of thumb scale for narrow angle meters is as follows:

DEVELOPMENT INDICATIONS FOR NARROW ANGLE LUMINANCE METERS (HONEYWELL)

Table 2.

Placed	Falls	Indicated Development		to render area in
III	XI	N—3	⎫	VIII
"	X	N—2	⎬ Contractions	"
"	IX	N—1	⎭	"
"	VIII	Normal		"
"	VII	N+1	⎫	"
"	VI	N+2	⎬ Expansions	"
"	V	N+3	⎭	"

EFFECT OF CONTRACTIONS AND EXPANSIONS
ON THE WHOLE SCALE

When a Zone IX is *developed to* a Zone VII as indicated by a $N-2$ symbol, *all* the zones are affected, but not *equally*. At the same time that the area exposed to Zone IX is *developed* to Zone VII, the areas exposed to Zone III remain in Zone III even though a $N-2$ *development* is given. (This is theoretically true, in practice the density of a negative exposed in Zone III and developed $N-2$ will be somewhat less but still in Zone III). The middle values change *less* than the high values, and *more* than the low values. A diagram will clarify this better than words.

EFFECT OF CONTRACTIONS

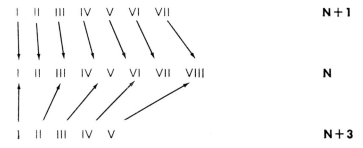

EFFECT OF EXPANSIONS

Plus developments or *Expansions* by as many as five zones are possible with some films; minus developments, or *Contractions* by as many as five zones are possible with some other films. *Ansco's Versapan* is remarkably responsive to variable development. It allows N+4 to N−2 with Edwal FG7. With developer D-23 it allows N+3 to N−5.

We can restate the basic rules of thumb for development determinations. The contrast range of the subject is measured in zones. The actual number of zones as compared to an upper limit of Zone VII for wide angle meters and zone VIII for narrow angle meters indicates the development time in symbols, to produce a Normal Print.

VARIABLE DEVELOPMENT INDICATIONS WITH OTHER LUMINANCE METERS

With other meters to determine the subject contrast range, and from that, determine the film *development indications* it is necessary to again work from *exposure* indications based on Zone V. (See pages 24 and 25.)

The procedure is an extension of the method started in the section on "exposure determinations for other meters." The simplest way to determine subject contrast range is to count in zones by the shutter speeds alone.

For development determinations two readings are necessary "shadow" and highlight. We will use an example in which the exposure indicated for the "shadow" is 1/10 second and the reading for the highlight is 1/200 second. In the diagram below the Roman numerals stand for Zones as previously and the fractions for exposures.

Example A

I	II	III	IV	V	VI	VII	VIII	IX
		1/50	1/25	1/10				A. Shadow placed
		Placed						in III
				1/200				B. Indicated high
					1/100			value exposure
						1/50		C. High value
								Falls in VII

When 1/50 is taken as the terminating figure for counting to the right, the highlight value falls in Zone VII. If a wide angle meter is used, a Normal development is indicated. On the other hand, if a narrow angle meter is used, a N+1 development is indicated.

Perhaps another example would be useful. The "shadow" reads 1/10 and the highlight area reads 1/800 second.

Example B

I	II	III	IV	V	VI	VII	VIII	IX
		1/50	1/25	1/10				
			1/800					
				1/400				
					1/200			
						1/100		
							(1/50)	

In this case the indicated development is either N−1 or N−2 according to which meter is used, wide angle or narrow respectively.

4. Previsualization And Variable Film Development

While variable film development is today a specialist practice, the adjustment of development time to compensate for a wide variety of subject contrast ranges is still the most effective way to control rendering. *Through variable film development the intentions of the photographer can be crystalized in the negative.*

The major aim of this chapter is to allow the reader to see for himself *how the "zone" can be used as a unit of measurement for development* as well as exposure. In the process he can also expect to observe the fundamental effects that different development times bring about over the entire scale of the print. It is this overall change in the print value scale that previsualization must cope with when variable development time is contemplated as a means of rendering an interpretation of a scene or subject.

1. Find a subject of average contrast range, in this case approximately 9 zones.

2. Set the film speed index into the meter for the film of your choice.

3. Place an 18% reflectance value card prominently in the scene. This card will be used as the standard value area for comparisons throughout this demonstration.

4. Take a meter reading of the card and plan to give the indicated exposure. (This is equivalent, for most meters, of *placing* the rendering of the grey card in Zone V.)

5. Read the other values in the scene and note where they *Fall.*

6. EXPOSURE

A. Expose 3 sheets of film at the indicated exposure. (Equivalent to a Zone V *Placement* of the 18% card).

B. Expose 1 sheet of film at twice the original exposure. (This is equivalent to *Placing* the meter reading of the 18% card in Zone VI.)

If roll film is being used, expose *ALL* the frames of 3 rolls to a Zone V placement. Then expose ALL the frames of 1 roll to a Zone VI placement. (The reason behind exposing all the frames is to keep the demonstration procedure identical to usual practice.)

7. DEVELOPMENT.

A. Develop *one* of the sheets, or rolls, exposed to Zone V according to the manufacturer's recommendations, or your own usual development time in your customary developer. Label it negative #1.

B. Develop the sheet or roll exposed to Zone VI also according to the manufacturer's recommendations or your own customary practice. Label it negative, #2.

C. Develop the remaining sheets or rolls thus:
   1. One sheet or roll at 1½ times the recommended development time.
   2. One sheet or roll at 2 times the recommended development time.

8. PRINTING

Set the enlarger for 8 x 10 prints. Use a #2 contrast grade of your usual printing paper. Give all the prints of this demonstration 3 minutes in the developer, 30 seconds in the stop bath, and 7 minutes in the acid fix, wash and dry.

A. Adjust the exposure of negative #1, or a frame from the roll #1, by means of test strips until a print is obtained in which the 18% grey card rendering in the print matches the card itself. Make print and label it print #1.

B. Note the negative exposure time for the matching print. *Treat this exposure time as a standard and use it exclusively for all negative exposures for the rest of this demonstration.*

C. Print negative #2 (the one exposed to Zone VI) at the newly found standard exposure. Processing must also be the same as given at step A. No dodging, no alterations of any kind in processing time; print on the same grade of #2 projection paper, same development, temperature, same every thing. Otherwise the prints may be useless for comparison later. Label this print, #2.

D. Expose and print the rest of the negatives in the same manner as at A. and C. Label later as indicated below.

9. COMPARISON OF PRINTS

A. Compare the values in the #1 print with those in the #2 print. Note how *all* the values, from Zone I through Zone IX, of corresponding areas are one zone lighter, in the #2 print.

B. Of the two remaining prints pick out the *one* whose grey card rendering comes the closest to matching the value of the grey card as rendered in the *Zone IV exposure (print #2).* Quite possibly *one* will match or almost match. Label it print #3.

C. One is looking at two prints, in #2 print the grey card was *exposed* for Zone VI, in the #3 print the grey card area was *"developed to"* Zone VI. The term "developed to" is used in conjunction with reading development times in "Zones."

D. Compare all the values, especially the dark values of prints #1, #2, and then #3. Note how the value renderings differ in the #2 print and #3. The rendering is not alike. In the third one the *low values* are very similar to what is seen in the #1 print, but the *high values* are similar to what is seen in the #2 print. The *contrast* of the prints are different.

The extended development in this case is that of a film *exposed to Zone V and developed to Zone VI.* This is called a "one zone expansion." In the language of the zone system this would be symbolized as N+1. The "N" stands for the word "Normal." *Normal* is an exact development time, as will be shown later, that corresponds only roughly to what up to this point we have been calling the "usual" or manufacturer's recommended development time.

Warnings

The experimental doing-demonstration above is by no means foolproof. So a few of the problems that may be encountered are set out:

1. The differences in the prints made as above are not obvious ones, indeed they are subtle. Consequently, if one is not accustomed to scrutinizing prints, the differences may pass unnoticed.

2. If extremely fast films are used, the two times "usual" development may not make sufficient difference to produce a N+1 development. With medium speed films, 50 - 200 ASA, there should be no trouble.

The exercise above, if *carefully done,* will show the reader the nature of his materials so far as what a change of development by one zone can do. By study and memorizing of the value changes over the entire scale of the three prints, one can get enough knowledge of the materials in his camera to start previsualizing the effect of altering development time.

Variable Development and Subject Contrast Control

One pronounced characteristic of the medium makes it possible to compensate for various subject contrasts by appropriate adjustment of film development time. This characteristic is that development affects the more densely exposed portions of the light sensitive emulsion than the barely exposed. The highly abstracted Hurter and Driffield photographic characteristic curves below indicate this fact.

Contrast control: that perennial problem of photography, as the old rule of thumb says, "Expose for the shadows and develop for the highlights."

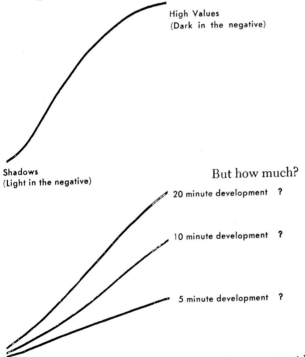

High Values
(Dark in the negative)

Shadows
(Light in the negative)

But how much?

20 minute development   ?

10 minute development   ?

5 minute development   ?

Before we answer these questions lets us consider the contrast problem as found in practice.

The contrast ranges of subjects are not all the same.
Some are Short

|·················|

Long

|···|

Medium

|······························|

And normal photographic paper has inherent contrasts that will accommodate or match only the medium subject contrast ranges.

|·····························|
|— — — — — — — — — — — — — - —|

Therefore we turn to the film and its development procedures to control the long and short contrast ranges. The light sensitive emulsions of photography react to development in a special way. Speaking of film now, in the shadow regions, the density remains thin no matter how long the film is developed. On the contrary high-value areas respond to increased development time vigorously; density increases rapidly as development is prolonged. See diagram below:

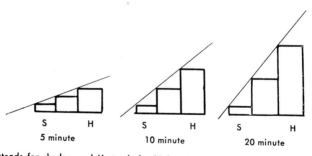

S stands for shadow and H stands for high values.
Note the angled lines here resemble the curves shown on the opposite page.

All this means that by stopping development at predetermined points we can control contrast in the negative more or less as we wish.

Consequently, if we expose our film to a short range contrast subject
|. . . . .| and develop the film long enough we can attain a negative that has, in effect, more contrast than the subject

|. . . . .| = subject contrast
|. . . . .| = negative contrast

And if we wish we can extend development until we have a negative whose contrast matches the contrast of photographic papers.

|. . . . .| = subject contrast
|. . . . .| = negative contrast
|— — — — — — — — — — — — —| = paper contrast

Conversely, we can expose the film to a long range subject contrast
|. . . . .|
shorten the film development time until its negative contrast matches the contrast of the paper.

|. . . . .|
|. . . . .| = negative contrast
|— — — — — — — — — — — — — — —| = paper contrast

All the above is very well in theory, but *how much* development? To measure we need some standard increment comparable, for example to the "inch." Obviously the "zone" and the 9 step grey scale is used .

| I | II | III | IV | V | VI | VII | VIII | IX |
Black   White

Next with this scale we can count contrast ranges in zones on any subject that we can measure. For example:

|. .|. .|. .|. .| (4 zones: a very short scale)
|. .|. .|. .|. .|. .|. .|. .|. .|. .|. .|. .|. .|. .|. .|. .|. .|. .|. .|
        (18 zones: a very long scale)

|··|··|··|··|··|··|··|··|··|

9 zones: a medium scale)

With Normal established at 9 zones, we can measure development time for the longer and shorter contrast ranges in zones. For example a shorter than normal contrast range of 8 zones would require "1 zone's worth" more development time to yield a negative that would print the full complement of 9 zones. In the zone system such development is called "Normal plus 1" and symbolized as N+1.

|··|··|··|··|··|··|··|··| = 8 zones subject contrast

Negative contrast developed to

|··|··|··|··|··|··|··|··|··| = 9 zones

which fits the paper contrast full scale

|─ |─ |─ |─ |─ |─ |─ |─ |─ | = 9 zone print contrast

Take another example: a 11 zone subject contrast range; this would indicate 2 less zones development to compensate for the excessive contrast. It is symbolized as N—2.

Symbols such as N—1, or N+2, etc. must be used because your favorite film and developer combination may require different times to achieve the required contrasts, as compared to some other combination. The section on testing will cover the practical calibrations by which development times are arrived at for these symbols.

Obviously one has choices in rendering the subject contrast in a given photograph. Perhaps you do not want all subjects to be rendered in the full white-to-black scale of the photographic printing paper. If so you can measure the number of zones that you do wish to show — providing that you take as a point of departure the Normal print. Just as one can measure anything in feet and inches, choice is wide open to the user of the zone system if he abides by the standards.

Figure 7A

THE EFFECT OF NORMAL DEVELOPMENT on a subject of low contrast need not yield a Normal Print. In the reproduction above the black circle and the dirty white wood show about the same four zone difference that was read on the exposure meter. Note the black line and the white lock (both unmeterable). These serve as the "Black & White Keys." And with them the print as a whole approaches the Normal Print because the photograph is full-substance and nearly full-scale.

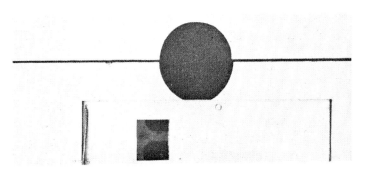

Figure 7B

THE EFFECT OF N+2 DEVELOPMENT ON THE SAME SUBJECT yields a print that comes close to the appearance of a Normal Print. And *without* the obvious inclusion of the black and white keys.

If the Normal Print is always thought of as a point of departure, or standard of comparison, technique always remains at the service of purpose and interpretation. If the Normal Print is thought of as the ultimate in print quality, technique becomes sterile and the closing of doors.

5. Stages Of Previsualization

The first stage of previsualization concerns the placement of a single meter reading opposite the Print Zone of your choice. (This is on the exposure meter of course.) Now since placement, generally, determines exposure of the film, this first stage deals with the exposure problem. And since placement choice is open, previsualization requires an act of imagination.

For example in Figure 8 the large grey patch is arbitrarily assigned a luminance value, or meter-reading as it is familiarly called, of 12. It so happens that this patch matches the Print Zone V in the grey scale on the left. If exposed so its own tone is to be reproduced, the 12 reading would be placed opposite Zone V on the meter. (One will grasp all this better if a meter is at hand for reference.)

But one can choose to render the patch in any one of the other 9 zones. Mechanically this may be done by simply placing the luminance value 12 opposite some other Zone, for instance Zone VIII and exposing as indicated. Imaginatively, however, one does something else first; one stares at the patch until it seems Zone VIII right in your eye.

The patch can be visualized, just as well, as a Zone III; if so let the imagination work the magic for you and the patch will grow darker in your mind's eye until the tone of Zone III is "seen." If one wishes to derive the benefits of previsualization, only after the magic happens does one Place the meter reading opposite the Zone III, or Zone VIII, or other Print Zone, and expose as the Placement indicates for that choice.

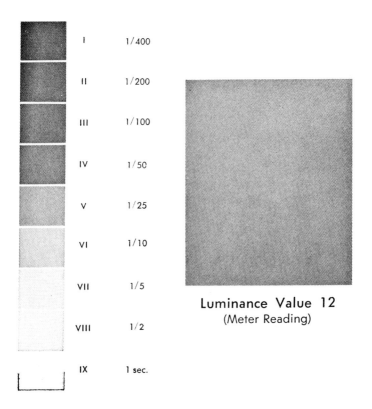

I	1/400	
II	1/200	
III	1/100	
IV	1/50	
V	1/25	
VI	1/10	
VII	1/5	
VIII	1/2	
IX	1 sec.	

Luminance Value 12
(Meter Reading)

Figure 8

ONE LUMINANCE VALUE MAY BE RENDERED IN ANY ONE OF THE 9 PRINT ZONES. The grey patch above is arbitrarily said to have meter reading of 12. It can be rendered as any one of the Print Values by placing the 12 opposite any chosen Zone on the meter and exposing as indicated. The series of exposures printed beside the column to the left are those indicated for a film rated as ASA 64 and for an aperture consistently held at f/8.

The first stage of previsualization is the stern kindergarten of intuitive seeing and perception from which no one graduates before learning.

One starts by identifying tones. In the example below, the tone of the roof matches one of the greys in Zone V on the meter dial.

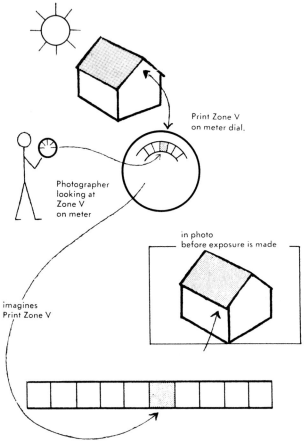

Print Zone V
on meter dial.

Photographer
looking at
Zone V
on meter

imagines
Print Zone V

in photo
before exposure is made

THE 1st STAGE IN PREVISUALIZATION

TONAL IDENTIFICATION

One can choose to place any one luminance value on, or in, any one zone, but what governs the choice in the first place? In the last analysis this is up to the individual. As a point of departure, however, we can present a Normal standard based on more or less literal renditions. For example Caucasian skin in sunlight is rendered with an amazing illusion of reality as a Print Zone VI. Once learned it is thereafter easy to mentally tag such a subject as a Zone VI for future reference. Obviously such a transference in the mind of a remembered one of grey to a flesh and blood subject, or visa versa, is never going to be very exact. However, because tonal identification is always subjective, tonal identification of subjects is one of the links between the art and science in photography.

Two interacting factors are forever present here: inherent tonality of the subject as exemplified by a lump of coal as compared to an orange; and the intensity and quality of the light present. With training the eye and mind can distinguish some degree of difference between inherent tonality and light intensity but the exposure meter never does. So the eye learns to see the difference in terms of zones, and translates for the meter.

Since Print Zones are symbolized by standardized shades of grey the degree of greyness can be memorized. And in starting to learn the Zone System associating shades of grey with the appropriate Roman numerals must be done. Memorizing the standardized shades of grey with their corresponding Roman numerals must be done because the Roman numeral is the link by which the tonalities and luminance in the visible world are converted and imagined in terms of Print Values. *In practice, as one looks at a subject, consciously identifies the tones according to the memorized shades of grey, and as one calls off the Roman numerals to himself, e.g. "Zone VI skin in sunlight" or "Zone V sky and Zone III shadows" one automatically starts to imagine a photograph while looking at the scene.*

The identification of tonalities and their assignment to zones is not a simple process because both physiological and psychological factors affect the photographer's decisions. Among the physiological reactions, the effect of the degree of contrast between adjacent tones is worth noting because the greater the degree of contrast the less likely one will be able to identify them as the camera will. The classic example is the middle grey square surrounded by black in one case and white in the other. While a person may know that the center grey is, say, a Zone V middle grey, in the former case he will see the grey as lighter than Zone V, in the latter case darker.

Another example is the case of deep black beside pure white, both seem more intense in this situation than if separated by a few middle greys. The eye will tend to see a Zone III grey as black when seen beside a Zone VIII pale grey. The camera, however, makes no such adjustment. Man's mental "grey scale" fluctuates.

On the psychological side, tonal identification is affected by man's habit of letting his idea of anything tell him what he is seeing in spite of what his eyes report. Take the *idea* of black for example: ink, hearses, coal, sirens in skin-tight gowns, dress suits and a thousand other associations all help form the idea of black. As far as tone value is concerned there is such a large number of dark greys called "black" that we can honestly say that for man black is itself a zone. His mental "grey scale" fluctuates unpredictably.

Because individual associations are so variable and so unpredictably affect each person's tonal identification, all that can be done here is to generalize. The list of Print Values and Subject Matter, prepared by Ansel Adams, refers to general tonal identification of some subject matter coupled with a generally acceptable "realistic" rendition of these subjects in photographs.

TABLE OF PRINT VALUES, SUGGESTING ZONES, OF SUBJECTS REALISTICALLY RENDERED

LOW VALUES

Zone I — The blackest black that a print can be made to yield. Doorways and windows opening into unlit rooms.

Zone II — First discernable tone above total black; the darkest part of the picture in which sense of space is required.

Zone III — Average dark materials, black clothes, leathers, etc., in the print will show adequate detail, creases, folds . . .

MIDDLE VALUES

Zone IV — Average dark foliage, dark stone, landscape shadow. Recommended shadow value for portraits in sunlight.

Zone V — Clear North sky as rendered by panchromatic film. Dark or sunburned skin in sunlight, grey stone, average weathered wood. "Middle value" of the grey scale, representing 18% reflectance value.

Zone VI — Caucasian skin with sunlight falling on it, but not with glare or highlights. Skin in portraits made entirely in the shade or overcast lighting. Clear North sky with orthochromatic film. Snow in shadow when both sun and shadow are in same picture.

Zone VII   Very light skin, either in sun or when entirely in shade. Average snow in raking sun. Light grey concrete, bright colors. Whites with textures and delicate values.

Zone VIII   Glaring white surfaces. Snow in flat sunlight, whites without texture, blank.

WHITE

Zone IX   Represented in print as the pure white of the paper base.

THE 2nd STAGE OF PREVISUALIZATION

Rare are the one luminance value scenes such as we isolated in the 1st Stage. But in all other instances after *one* meter reading is Placed, the photographer is to observe where the rest of the meter readings line-up. In the accompanying diagram the 50 was Placed to match, and the 400 and 13 are seen to FALL (as this is called) opposite Zones VIII and III respectively.*

After observing where the meter readings of the unplaced tones of the original FALL, the photographer is to compare them to his mental identification of the original tones. Because the Placed value happens to match the original, the rest need not. Where matching fails the meter indicates to the photographer in what Print Zone he should imagine these values of the original. For example, in the diagram opposite the 13 stands for shadow; in most instances the eye will see brighter detail than will show in the Zone III rendering indicated. Consequently reference to the meter enables one to know how much darker (in this case) to imagine the tones than the eye sees. Extend such previsualization to as many tones in the original as feasible.

---

*On the Weston Model V the numbers 10, 13 and 8 correspond to 50, 400, 13 respectively on the earlier models.

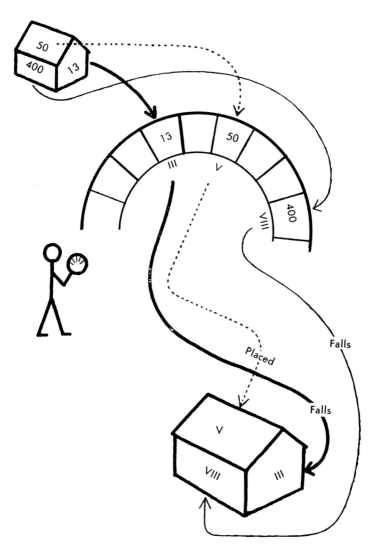

THE 2nd STAGE IN PREVISUALIZATION

The Arabic numerals refer to the Weton Master IV.

THE 3rd STAGE OF PREVISUALIZATION

In the 3rd stage of previsualization the photographer generally grapples with the effect of development on those exposure zones that "fall" instead of the "placed" one. And he has some small range of choice open to him. Due to the nature of the light sensitive emulsions of photography, exposure zones "falling" opposite Print Zone V and higher on the meter can be "developed to" the Print Values of one's choice.

For example: if patch A, seen in Figure 9, with a luminance value of 6.5 were "placed" in Zone III, then patch B with a luminance value, or meter reading, of 50 would "fall" opposite Zone VI.° By altering the development time the grey of patch B can be rendered in any one of the Print Values V through IX, whichever one chooses, and still render the grey of patch A within the boundaries of Print Value III. The development symbols in the diagram are all based on a film rated at ASA 64, exposed so that patch A is rendered in Zone III, namely f/8 at 1/25 second.

Previsualization at this stage is complicated by the fact that various development times of a film do not affect all the Print Zones equally. For example with short contrast range subjects the additional development time usually given to compensate "spreads" a limited number of exposure zones over all 9 Print Zones. This class of development time is called EXPANSIONS. Conversely in scenes of long contrast range the exposure zones are "condensed" into the 9 Zones. This class of development times is called CONTRACTIONS. A schematic description is given below to show, in a general way, how each zone in a contrast range has to be previsualized with a few sample development times.

°On the Weston Model V numbers 7 and 10 correspond to the 6.5 and 50 respectively found on the I to IV models.

A

Luminance Value 50 (Weston IV)

If Placed →

B

Luminance Value 6.5 (Weston IV)

can be developed
to any of these →

I

II

III

IV

N−1   V

N   VI

N+1   VII

N+2   VIII

N+3   IX

Figure 9

Luminance Values rendered in pre-selected Zones by film development. With Patch A, meter reading 6.5, placed in Zone III (exposure f/8 1/25 second) Film Speed ASA 64, Patch B can be rendered in Zones V to IX as indicated by the development symbols beside the various Zones. With any development from N-1 to N+3 the grey of Patch A will be rendered within the limits of Zone III. (The Arabic numbers refer to **Weston Master IV's**.)

EFFECT OF CONTRACTIONS

EFFECT OF EXPANSIONS

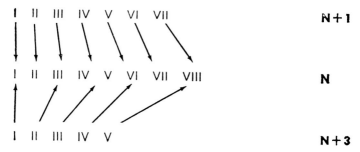

THE THIRD STEP IN PREVISUALIZATION deals with the effect of expansion and contraction development times on the middle zones.

Note that the change in development, which is indicated by the development symbols, effects the higher Zones most, the middle Zones less, and Zones I and II hardly at all. In the 3rd stage of previsualization the photographer may take all this into consideration.

DETERMINATION OF DEVELOPMENT TIME FROM THE METER

To get a preliminary indication of a development time to develop for a normal print, either Zone VII or VIII may be taken as the upper limit. In Figure 10 Zone VIII is shown as the point of departure. Note the extension of a line opposite VIII.

As has been said, page 27, a Zone VIII "textured white"

is feasible with narrow angle luminance meters. A Zone VII is better for the wide angle meters. (See page 27.)

In Figure 10 arc A shows the situation of a 5-zone subject brightness range; this is 3-zones less than 8. The solid and dotted lines together on arc A mean that if a film were exposed to a 5-zone subject contrast range and then given 3 zones more development than Normal for arbitrary example, 18 minutes instead of 10 then that negative would render the scene as if it originally had 8 zones of contrast. In other words, by an N+3 development a 5 zone contrast range is expanded to 8 zones, and in the print these 5 zones will be distributed over Print Values I through VIII.

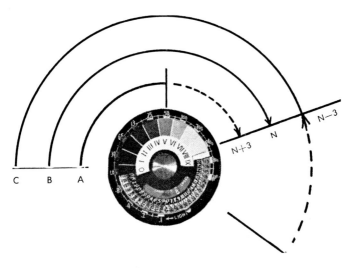

Figure 10

THE THIRD STAGE OF PREVISUALIZATION also pertains to the determination of the development time necessary to compensate for the prevailing subject contrast range.

Line A represents 5 zone brightness range.
Line B represents 8 zone brightness range.
Line C represents 11 zone brightness range.

If this much is understood we can turn our attention to the contractions as illustrated at line C, the 11 zones Subject Contrast range. Here less than Normal development is needed, and since 11 zones is 3 zones more than 8 then N−3. With some combinations of film and developer this time might be as little as 3 or 4 minutes. At arc C again the entire arc represents the metered Contrast Range and the dotted line indicates the amount of minus development that would be required to compensate so that a film exposed to contrast range of 11 zones, when printed, would, in effect, contract the 11 zones and distribute them between Print Values I and VIII. Such a 3 zone contraction is symbolized as N−3.

Warning: It must be remembered that these preliminary indications of developments are only starting points for calculations. Other considerations generally enter to change the actual development given.

CHART OF CONTRAST COMPENSATIONS TO YIELD "NORMAL" PRINTS

Contrast Range	Development Symbol
Etc.	Etc.
11 zones	N−3
10 zones	N−2
9 zones	N−1
8 zones	N
7 zones	N+1
6 zones	N+2
5 zones	N+3
Etc.	Etc.

The determination of the overall contrast range suggests a development time, and one which would render the scene as a full-scale, full-substance or Normal print. While one starts planning from this information, later considerations may change the final development time.

While variable film development is explained here and emphasized in the zone system, the control of scene contrast that is inherent in various types of film stock, developers both normal and special, and the various contrast grades of photographic paper is also subject to employment in units of zones. And any practioner of the zone system can so use them. While not complete, an indication of such control by papers and developers is given on page 93.

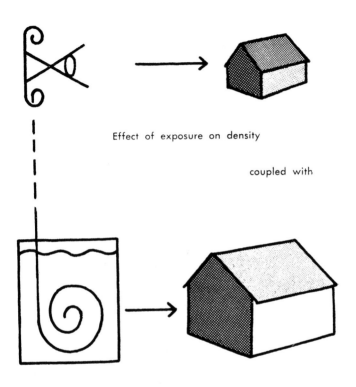

Effect of exposure on density

coupled with

effect of variable film development time on contrast

The photographer looking at his exposure meter can predict the tonal effect of changing development time from a standard.
And thereby "read" development time directly from the exposure meter.

THE 3rd STAGE OF PREVISUALIZATION

THE FOURTH STAGE OF PREVISUALIZATION

The fourth stage of previsualization pertains to how one wishes to render an event in front of the camera.

The first three stages of previsualization are concerned frequently with the mechanics of imagining a Normal print out of whatever contrast problem the scene at hand presents. That known, one may then begin to evolve what else can be done with it. From many subjects more than one rendering, and convincing renderings at that, will be imaginable. And because one of the hidden renderings will fit his purpose better than all the rest, the work of the 4th stage is to previsualize, in succession, all the potential renderings that a scene, like a bud, hides within itself.

Whatever his purpose, whether towards capturing the realism of outward facts, or whether, conversely, to make the facts in front of the camera mirror some inner realism, previsualization leads to finding which one rendering will materialize his intentions.

The photographer may wish to preserve a sense of the literal, a faithfulness to the visible event in the world of appearances; or he may wish to depart in the direction of stylization, or again in the direction of "abstraction" or the "non-objective."

By previsualizing every potential in the scene the beginner can choose the one which lucidly states his interpretative purpose. With considerable practice, for some individuals, previsualization of the precisely lucid rendering will become intuitive.

The potentials of a scene contain its own limitations and how the medium is bound to transform the subject adds more; nevertheless, at one extreme the photographer can aim previsualization at recording literally and be assured of considerable success — and know beforehand that in such instances his own purposes will be overshadowed by the significance of the event or object. At the other extreme he can aim previsualization at the transformations by which the medium automatically metamorphoses everything that it touches. It is at this extreme that the purposes and intent of the photographer become the most evident in the image.

Then, once the photographer has decided on the rendering, his choice is made manifest by three crisp directions to himself that he follows on the spot: f-stop, shutter speed and development symbol.

f/8   f-stop

1/25   Shutter Speed

N + 2   Development Symbol

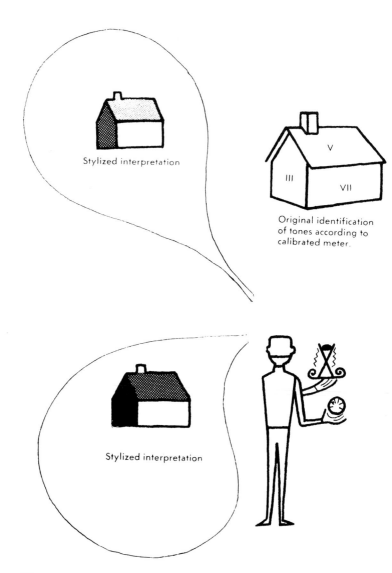

Stylized interpretation

Original identification
of tones according to
calibrated meter.

Stylized interpretation

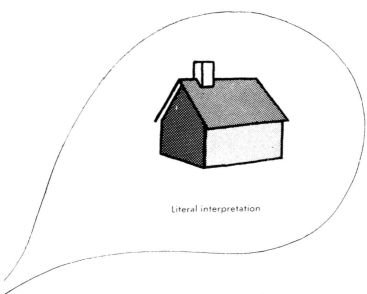

Literal interpretation

THE 4th STAGE OF PREVISUALIZATION

To see in the mind's eye all the possible renditions that the subject and medium permit. And to choose on purpose one rendering to actualize.

The fourth stage of previsualization is the act of looking at a scene and imagining all the possible renderings that the light sensitive material makes available with that specific subject. This act is ordinarily done after meter readings have been made and all the potential combinations of exposure and development have been studied. With all the data at hand one may previsualize in the direction of realism or towards stylization or into "abstraction" according to one's creative purposes.

The reason why the photographer previsualizes, in succession, all the potential renderings of the subject is so that he can select the one rendering he knows will best fulfill his own purposes with the subject at hand. This is the primary creative moment in photography.

6. Step By Step Outline

The outline below is presented step by step because such a manner is useful when learning how to put the theory and principles of the Zone System into effect. Later the use of the system will become so habitual and such a flexible tool that the immediate picture situation will always determine the order and number of steps. Eleven steps are named as follows:

1. Observe the subject
2. Start to previsualize by mentally identifying subject or brightness values as Print Values.
3. Take exposure meter readings of reflectances
4. Note meter reading in a sketch of the subject
5. Determine approximate contrast range in zones
6. Previsualize the potential tonal renditions. Determine interpretive direction either towards realism or stylizations on non-literal renderings.
7. Select one rendering and materialize it; with the directions called f-stop, shutter speed, development symbol.
8. Write all data into the Exposure Record or notebook.
9. Develop film by Time and Temperature.
10. Print remembering "Postvisualization."
11. Study the final print with data at hand.

1. SUBJECT OBSERVED

Only when a subject is considered picture-worthy is production to be undertaken.

Never treat a subject as an exercise ONLY. No matter how simple, or how exploratory, or how much one is tempted to treat the specific instance superficially as an exercise, come to all subjects expecting to contact reality.

Set the film speed in the Exposure Index window of the meter.

2. START TO PREVISUALIZE BY MENTALLY IDENTIFYING,

or tagging, with Zones, the various Luminances, in the scene and subject.

To become habitually familar with this step the following exercises are recommended. Make a medium sized step-wedge as seen on 21 and carry it around to familar objects and match the tones of familiar objects. Some sur-surprises are in store nevertheless when...it feels natural to say "Zone VI skin," or "Zone III chocolate" and to ask your wife in what Zone she likes her toast, you can leave the step-wedge behind.

3. TAKE EXTRA METER READINGS

always holding the meter so that it or the hand holding it does not cast a shadow on the area being metered.

At the start make extensive meter readings, for each photograph, of all luminances that can be reached. Try to locate 9 reflectances that represent each of the 9 Zones. This part of planning, when learning the Zone System, may be treated as opportunity to gain familiarity with the recurring brightness of the visual world: also to memorize the intensity of the prevailing light. Obviously extensive readings assures accurate previsualization over the entire tonal range and the whole future photograph's surface.

An exposure meter is a brainless instrument whose readings must be interpreted. Because the meter averages all light in its "Cone of Sight," all three of the circles above would read the same. Consequently only the right hand circle would give a useable reading. The moral of this illustration is to invariably select solid tones which are large enough area to be measured. The cone of sight of the Weston exposure meters is about a 30° angle with baffle closed. And about 55° when open.

When one remembers that flesh tones for example, in bright sunlight always reads the same — as well as a dozen or so other recurrent brightnesses, one can make fewer readings for each photograph.

Regarding the proper number of reflectance readings, familiarity with the prevailing contrast situation at the moment will govern; with well known tonal situations, few readings are required; with unfamiliar situations extensive readings are necessary. By rule of thumb three exposure readings are usually essential: important shadow, significant object, textured white.

A. Important Shadow

Important Shadow refers to the darkest part of the scene in which one demands detail and which will be rendered in Print Zone III or IV. One does not have to select the very darkest part of the scene visible to the eyes, nor does this area necessarily have to be in shadow. If one chooses a low middle grey for Important Shadow, the values lower than this on the meter will be lost in the blacks of the print. In many subjects there are dark areas in which the eye can easily see detail. Yet one can knowingly and purposefully submerge these details in blacks; either because, in a high-contrast range situation, the photographic materials can not hold this detail and at the same time retain the textured whites, or because, for purposes of interpretation, one deliberately chooses to lose details in Zone Zero black.

What one selects as the important shadow is a matter of personal choice and a choice that must be made afresh for each photograph. The beginner rarely has the slightest idea of what to select. He is advised to start with the darkest part of the scene in which he can distinguish detail for his *important shadow*. Experience will reveal the possible deviations.

B. Significant Object (or Important Object)

Significant Object refers to that object which the photographer insists be in the tone of his own choosing even if other values of the picture must be sacrificed.

The significant object more often than not is a middle grey, but it may be a shadow area, or on the contrary as high as textured white. Whatever tone it is, this is a handy starting point for previsualizing quickly.

When the beginner thinks that he can have more than one tone in precisely the Zone he previsualizes, and at extremes of the scale, he must remember the limitations of the light sensitive emulsions. He can place any one, single significant object reading in any zone he wishes: then, what is *lighter* in the original will be *lighter* in the print, and what is *darker* in the original will be *darker* in the print. The various tones may be made to come closer to each other or further apart, but, without the aid of filters with scenes containing areas of strong (or saturated) colors, tones can not be made to "cross over."

Zone VI Skin Value is frequently the Important Object.

This is a standard tonal value used in the Basic Photo Series. It refers to the tone of grey in which Caucasian skin is normally rendered, because Zone VI gives about the best illusion of such flesh in photographs. Since a face has planes that reflect differently, a standard is needed. This standard reading is made by turning the flat of the cheek to a 45° angle to the sun — or to whatever light source is in effect — and reading carefully. Caucasian skin tone varies about 1 Zone between dark-room-pallor to Alpine tan and should be so considered in planning the photograph.

C Textured White and White Key

Textured White refers to the bright parts of the scene in which detail is demanded. This tone is associated with Zone VII, or Zone VIII.

The high *values* of a scene must be distinguished from the "highlights" or White Keys. The latter are ordinarily too small to be measured and because they are very tiny spots in the print therefore require no detail. What the glitter of chrome or other metal actually measures is of no importance so long as it falls in Zone IX white or higher. The presence of highlights or white keys in a photograph with a long series of greys gives richness; or in a long series of textured whites the white keys give vitality. The effect of the white keys is to make the greys convincing. To see for yourself drop a white handkerchief in a scene containing only middle and lower greys. See Figure 7A and 7B.

4. NOTE EXPOSURE METER READINGS IN A SKETCH

The sketch should be highly diagrammatic—no more than the large tonal areas indicated. With Arabic numerals write in the luminance readings within the boundaries of the sketch outlines. Write a "P" beside the PLACED value. This determines exposure. To record the planned development, write the appropriate Roman numerals outside the boundaries of the sketch outline. Where all the readings *fall* can be determined from the Arabic numerals, when necessary. The Roman numerals indicate in what Print Zone you expect the various reflectance areas to print.

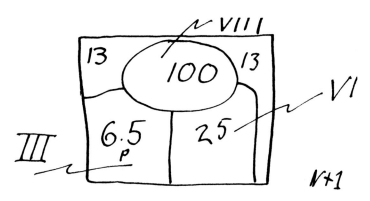

Of the many ways of keeping a record of all data and calculations needed for a photograph, two are recommended: the rough sketch and the Exposure Record. An example of the Exposure Record appears on page 67. The first is advised when first learning to previsualize; the second is a time saver when one can visualize tones with the Roman numeral symbols for the zones.

In the example above, note placement in Print Zone III makes the other exposure zones fall in Zone IV, V and VII but the N+1 development will render these reflectances in zones IV½, VI and VIII respectively.

5. DETERMINE APPROXIMATE SUBJECT CONTRAST RANGE IN UNITS OF ZONES

Place the lowest luminance reading opposite Zone I on the exposure scale and count off the difference, in zones, to the highest reading. (If the lowest luminance reading contains important textures, place this reading opposite Zone III and count off as before.) The contrast range of the scene may be as little as one zone or upward of fifteen. This approximate determination of contrast range has a limited use: it is used only to give a *general* idea of what development time might be expected. With for example, a literal interpretation in mind, with contrast ranges falling between seven and nine zones Normal development might be anticipated. Below seven zones expansion is probably in order; above nine zones contraction may be necessary.

6. PREVISUALIZE THE POTENTIAL RENDERINGS

To speed up the selection of the rendering closest to intentions, know before hand whether one will make a literal interpretation or some obviously stylized departure.

The sequence of previsualization and subsequent planning of the photograph starts with the PLACED value in order to determine exposure. Then proceeds to observe the contrast range of subject, as that is determined by where the rest of the values, or exposure zone readings, FALL. From this development time is planned.

1. Placement determines exposure.
   A. Important Object — exposure zone reading of same is placed opposite the Zone of one's choice;
       or
   B. Important Shadow — placed opposite Zone III or IV;
       or
   C. Textured White — is placed opposite Zone VII, or VIII, depending on type of meter. See page 27.

2. Development time is planned from the contrast range of the subject as that is determined by where the rest of the exposure zone readings FALL. (At this stage development time is considered only in its symbolic form. For example N—3 stands for a certain number of minutes of development; but because the time differs for each film and its developer combination, a symbol is more workable than the actual time in minutes.) Actual developing time is determined by tests.

3. Adjustments planned to obtain the rendering desired — or however the nature of subject and materials alters one's preferences. For example:

The Important Object, skin in sunlight reads exposure zone 400. We want to render this in Print Zone VI. A cloud in the same scene reads 1600 and a dark coat in a shadow reads exposure zone 13. The visual indication would appear on the meter thus:

```
  I   II   III   IV   V   VI   VII   VIII   IX
 13  ............... 400 ..... 1600 (Weston Master IV)
```
(Underline isolates the PLACED value.)
```
  8  ...............  13  .....   15  (Weston Master V)
```

Previsualized for a Normal development, which the contrast range of 13 to 1600 suggests, dark-coat-in-shadow would be lost in black, as would all substances reflecting Luminances of 25 and 50 (Or stated in terms of Print Zones, all substances which fell on or below Zone III would be lost in black.) The skin and cloud would be rendered as desired. If the sacrifice of the dark coat and shadow can be made without destroying the photograph, Normal development and exposure as determined by the placement of 400 "in" VI will fulfill the purpose.

In this situation sacrifice is not the only alternative: previsualize exposure zone 13 opposite Zone III. (Zone III is the lowest Zone in which detail will appear. Zone III is sometimes called "Textured Black.") The new positions seen on the meter would appear thus:

	I	II	III	IV	V	VI	VII	VIII	IX	X	XI
Weston IV			13	. . . .					400	. .	1600

(13 is now the PLACED value.)

	I	II	III	IV	V	VI	VII	VIII	IX	X	XI
Weston V			8	. . . .					13	. .	15

With Normal development both flesh and cloud would be lost in white. But they can be rendered in their former Print Zones by reducing development of the negative by 3 zones. To indicate a N—3 action arrows are used as below:

	I	II	III	IV	V	VI	VII	VIII	IX	X	XI
. . . .			13	. . . .					400	. .	1600

/◀—————————

/◀—————————

(For the sake of illustration it is assumed that the value placed in III will remain in that Zone with a N—3 development.)

The instances where one's desired renderings must be altered somewhat are many, and the illustration above but one of many possibilities.

Subjects having normal reflectance contrast ranges (7, 8 and 9 zones) will ordinarily respond the most convincingly to extremes of placement and development—from N—3 to N+5. Contrast ranges 10 zones or above lend themselves to over-scale stylizations; whereas contrast ranges of 6 zones or under may look "muddy" rather than be thought stylizations, unless expanded development times are given.

7. SELECT THE DESIRED RENDERING AND MATERIALIZE IT

Materialize the planned rendering with the three directions; f-stop, shutter speed, and development symbol. (It is assumed that the Exposure Index of the film in the camera has been set in the meter.)

Regarding the creative aspect: during previsualization the creativity comes to a climax as one specific rendering is settled on and the subject is envisioned in the tonalities of its own photograph. While one works out the practical calculations, the creative activity may be lessened, even absent. However, for the moment of exposure creative intensity is again brought to bear and held at a peak. Thereafter the intensity may gradually subside — if one is an accomplished photographer the intensity may be cut off abruptly. But exposure must always, as Edward Weston said, "Sum up all that a man is at that moment."

This intensely aware state of mind must be renewed at the time of printing, in order to remember precisely the previsualization at the moment of exposure.

8. WRITE ALL DATA DOWN IN THE EXPOSURE RECORD

When one has outgrown the need of sketches for planning photographs, the Exposure Record provides a compact check list for planning and handy way of keeping all pertinent data. A sample sheet is reproduced on page 67.

To use the Exposure Record write the luminance readings in the squares under the appropriate Print Zones. The PLACED value should be indicated as such in some manner; it is circled on the sample. Actual readings should be indicated somehow, e.g. underlined, and written opposite the zones in which they Fall on the meter. See line 1 in the sample. To keep the data in the Exposure Record in harmony with the situation on the exposure meter write in ALL the exposure zone numbers whether they have been read or not. (Line 3 on the sample.) To indicate the effect of other than Normal development arrows are used which lead from the zone in which the reading *falls* to the zone in which one expects to render it by development. See lines 6 and 8 of the sample.

On lines 5 and 6 we see how the previous example of face, cloud and coat-in-shadow would be written into the Exposure Record. On line 5 the notation for Normal development appears. The 64 stands for the *Film speed.* The 8" stands for the Focal Length of the lens. No bellows EXTension was used so a dash appears under the first "X." No filter was used so dash marks appear under *No.*

EXPOSURE RECORD

Designed and Copyright by

ANSEL ADAMS

Morgan & Morgan, Publishers

SHEET NO. 1
FILM: Tri X
SIZE: 4 x 5
DATE LOADED: 1/2/65
DATE EXPOSED: Same

PLACEMENT OF SUBJECT INTENSITIES ON EXPOSURE SCALE

REL. LENS STOP f/	64	45	32	22	16	11	8	5.6	4	2.8
REL. EXP. FOR V	1/32	1/16	1/8	1/4	1/2	1	2	4	8	16
REL. EXP. FOR I	1/2	1	2	4	8	16	32	64	128	256
WESTON SCALE	—	U	—	—	—	↓	C	—	D	—

NO.	SUBJECT	ZONES	0	I	II	III	IV	V	VI	VII	VIII	IX	FILM TYPE OR SPEED	F. L.	EXT.	x	NO.	x	STOP	x	EXP.	DEVELOPMENT
1	Example of Notation	65	65								⑥⁰₀											
2	" "																					
3	" "		65	13	26	60	100	200	400	⑱₀	ⁱ⁄₉₉											
4																						
5	Face + Cloud		6.5					④⁰⁰	⑱₀			64	8″	1	-	1	-	16	5₀	✓	
6	" " "					⑥₆			400	ⁱ⁄₆₀	1/₆₀	"	1	-	1	-	11	7₀	N-3	
7																					
8	Signboard - Close-up			1/6	3.2	6.4	13	↑			64	"	1	-	1	-	5.6	2₅	N+3	
9																					
10																					
11																					
12																					

PHOTOGRAPHER: PLACE: JOB: REMARKS OVERLEAF

67

(Number) and X. 16 represents f/16 under STOP and 50 represents 1/50 second shutter speed under *EXP*. The development is given by the symbol N. On the overleaf are lines for further *Remarks*.

In line 6 note that a slant line appears in the film type column and 1600 written in the bottom half. This is a way of indicating that the square is used for Zone notation rather than film speed. The empty upper half indicates Zone X and the lower represents Zone XI.

Five sets of relationships are tabulated in the squares above the *ZONES*. On the line marked Weston Scale the dashes and letters and arrow are the same as found on the inner dial of the Weston meter. (It would be possible to superimpose a ten step grey scale in this row of squares.) *Relative Exposure for Zone I* means that if the amount of exposure which was required to get a Zone I density in the negative is taken as a unit of 1, then to obtain a density of Zone II twice as much exposure would be required; for Zone III density four times as much exposure and so on in geometric progression up to 256 times that unit of exposure for Zone IX density.
Relative Exposure for Zone V means that the unit is that amount of exposure required to obtain a Zone V density in the negative. Four times such exposure would produce a Zone VII, whereas 1/16 that exposure would produce a Zone I.

Relative Lens Stop F/ shows the diaphragm opening marking in relation to zones and the 1:2 ratio. If f/45 at a given shutter speed gave a Zone I density in the negative then f/32, at the identical shutter speed, would give a Zone II density and so on in the 1:2 ratio progression. These various relationships are useful in various aspects of testing and to plan photographs with other than Weston exposure meters.

9. DEVELOP FILM BY TIME & TEMPERATURE

The temperature of the film developer is standardized at the customary 68° (higher if working in the tropics). The actual time in minutes is determined by tests as given later in Section 7.

10. PRINT, REMEMBERING TO "POSTVISUALIZE"

While remembering the previsualization image, print to match. Print as simply and directly as possible. If no errors have been made, the negatives have the contrast and densities appropriate to the mentally held image. Consequently printing exposures are CONSISTENTLY at a minimum and manipulations likewise because they too were planned at exposure.

A resurgence of the creative state of mind is desirable at the time of printing because the intensity so "built up" is actually necessary to recall the purpose and previsualized image while printing. This self induced state may be called "postvisualization." The negative is thought of as a kind of score to be performed and the kind of creativity native to the concert performer is apropos at printing.

11. STUDY THE PRINT WITH ALL DATA PRESENT

A. Take the print back to the original scene and compare. Observe if the previsualization is materialized tone by tone as planned. With the data completely recorded in both sketch and Exposure Record agreements and disagreement can be checked; the reasons for mistakes can be located promptly. In the Polaroid system such comparison on the spot is automatic — and indeed eye-opening! Hence the reason for suggesting a direct comparison of the planned photograph with the original. There is no better way of getting acquainted with the nature of the materials; nor any better way of coming to grips with visual interpretation. Compare, and never forget how much the most realistic photograph is an interpretation of the original.

B. Study the print for fulfillment of intentions other than the tonal rendering. You selected that particular rendering over the rest for a reason, and the reason might as well be significant. Ask and answer these questions: "Is this interpretation embedded in the photograph faithful to my intentions and purposes? Or am I rationalizing?" If the answer is in the negative, ask some more questions. "Is this accidental interpretation true to myself? Can I honestly say that it is a part of me, even in spite of its failing to meet my demands?" If not — the wastebasket is one alternative; the other is to make over your inner man until he corresponds to the statement of the photograph!

C. Study the print as if it were a new visual fact, independent of your planning, camera and everything connected with you. Study the print as if through the eyes of other people. Disassociate yourself from your own photograph. Look at it as if were made by another. In so doing the photograph may soon discover something for you. Something in the world at large, or conversely something in yourself. *Visualize the photograph back to the original.* In the condition of creativeness called now *Visualization,* both "pre" and post," photographs sometimes achieve the status of mirrors that can be walked into.

As is implied above, B and C merge. Perhaps they repeat each other. Perhaps they repeat the same thing, namely that the vital *is-ness* surrounding *Visualization* does not stop with exposure. Such creativeness is induced again while printing. Return to the same state repeatedly while studying photographs. The ultimate achievement of the practice of the Zone System is a creative continuity leading towards communication-evocation in other people and towards the next photograph.

"Communication" is a common word in photography the meaning of which, in a way, "pulsates" between the brute transmission of facts as only photography can, to tenuous, invisible, inadequate-but-sufficient interchanges of spirit. The words "creative continuity" have a bearing on the last. With these two words we include, as seen in the diagrams, the alive viewer and his "creativeness."

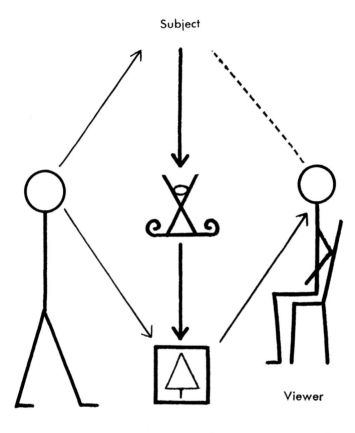

Subject

Photographer Photograph

Viewer

When the viewer is a part of the cycle, his linkage back to the original subject is never as strong as the photographer's when the latter plays the role of viewer. Hence the dotted line. The photographer can purposely strengthen the viewer's linkage to subject with representational photos—or correctly weaken the linkage with photos in which the subject is barely or not recognizable. The cycle reads counter clockwise. The cycle, at times, also proceeds clockwise! And in the ultimate mystique of camera vision, or camera work, the cycle reads clockwise and counter clockwise simultaneously!

7. Testing Procedures

To base previsualization on firm craftsmanship, materials need to be coordinated with equipment, and both with the man.

The testing or calibration procedures outlined in detail here were originated by Nicholas Dean and Stephen Gersh. Slight modifications were made after tryouts in classes and workshops. So if the procedures are followed carefully, the whole system will be calibrated . . . and to the man. While performing the calibrations various short cuts will suggest themselves, but be patient and wait to try them out the next time that one needs to test a new film, or lens, or a new developer. It has been observed repeatedly that altering plans midstream in these tests cause many costly mistakes.

One may anticipate around 35 hours spread over a convenient period. That is, if the preplanning is accurate and the operations are fully prepared and precisely done. (Silly mistakes seem to gather for the occasion.) A large note book is desirable to keep all plans, outlines, data of every kind, negatives, prints and conclusions, including blunders.

One may also anticipate frustrations over the hidden shortcomings of our very expensive equipment.

The testing methods cover both roll and sheet film. Separate methods are given for use with and without densitometers. The latter called the "eye match" method is elaborated in this manual because few have access to densitometers.

THE 6 BASIC TESTS

1. STANDARD NEGATIVE PRINTING TIME
2. WORKING FILM SPEED
3. NORMAL DEVELOPMENT
4. BRIGHTNESS RANGE CHECK
5. EXPANSIONS
6. CONTRACTIONS

The objective of each of the 6 tests is as follows:

1. STANDARD NEGATIVE PRINTING TIME. To establish a short negative exposure time that is also optimum for the photographic printing paper selected for customary use. Such a printing time should be standard for any planned negative thereafter, and only slight variations anticipated to bring a print into final tonal balance.

With this test the luminance meter and shutter of the lens tested are calibrated and their discrepancies compensated for.

2. FILM SPEED. To take advantage of the highest possible speed of the film in question. To consistently produce negatives that print with the least possible exposure. To take advantage of the smaller grain effect of thin negatives.

Because the low densities of the negative are the least affected by small changes in development, the film speed test is always done before the development tests.

3. NORMAL DEVELOPMENT. To determine the exact developing time in minutes of any film and developer combination which will print nine consecutive brightness values in the subject in the nine zones of a print.

4. BRIGHTNESS RANGE CHECK. To make a practical check on the accuracy and validity under field or studio conditions of the first three tests.

5. EXPANSIONS. To find the "plus" development times, measured in zones, by which to compensate for subject brightness ranges of 7 zones or less.

6. CONTRACTIONS. To find the "minus" development times by which to control subject brightness ranges of 9 zones or more.

PREPARATIONS FOR TESTING

Everything required for testing should be on hand from the start, including certain special knowledge such as the ability to read luminance meters in zones, or time and temperature development of both film and photographic printing paper.

FILM. In date, sufficient quantity of same emulsion number. 24 rolls of the selected film, or 2 boxes of 25 sheets. Choose a film that one expects to use regularly for a year or more.

FILM DEVELOPER. Fresh, preferably use once and discard . . . both for tests and customary use. If replenishment for future work is decided upon, use a consistent plan of replenishment and stick to the plan.

PHOTOGRAPHIC PRINTING PAPER. With the roll film use the #3 contrast grade of enlarging paper, or its equivalent, for all testing. With sheet film standardize on the #2 medium contrast grade.

PAPER DEVELOPER. Very small quantities of fresh working solution for EACH test print and discard after one use.

EXPOSURE RECORD BOOK. Buy a large notebook for tabulating and preserving *all* negatives, prints and data for future reference. For example, when a new projection paper is to be tried out one has only to print the various negatives of the normal test to find a new normal time.

18% REFLECTANCE GREY CARD. Called a Neutral Test card, this is used as the target for exposure in all the tests. (Purchase at photo stores.)

PHOTOFLOODS. Fresh, either daylight or other, with reflectors and stands to hold them. Check and replace after three hours burning time.

EQUIPMENT CLEANED AND CHECKED

A. Tanks and Trays scrubbed.

B. Thermometer checked against a calibrated one.

74

C. "Zero" setting of luminance meter properly adjusted Preferably checked against a meter known to be accurate. Fortunately the Film Speed Test will compensate for meters that are off. If a Working Film Speed is arrived that is two or more stops off the recommended one, it may be suspected that the luminance meter is at fault.

D. The shutter of the lens used for the tests should be checked by a reliable and properly equipped shop. In unchecked shutters one must assume that *all* the speeds are different than marked. If it is impossible to have the shutters repaired or checked proceed with the testing as if everything were perfect. Any wide discrepancies in the various progressions of the testing *may be* the result of some freak shutter speed. But check the human errors first.

TIME AND TEMPERATURE PROCESSING. Both film and paper are developed at the standard temperature 68° for their appropriate number of minutes without any deviation whatsoever in either temperature or time. This must be especially watched while printing. For the latter use the manufacturer's development time, or 3 minutes and constant agitation.

STANDARD BLACK AND WHITE SQUARES. Because the blackest and the whitest any given photographic paper will yield can be made without recourse to special equipment, these are used as the basic starting points for the "eye match" method.

A. STANDARD BLACK. Use the enlarger as the light source. Set it at the height for an 8 x 10 enlargement from your size of negative. Set aperture at f/11, and expose for two minutes. Time and temperature development of the paper square. After 5 minutes in hypo store in fresh water to prevent any possible bleaching. These black squares should be made fresh for every testing session in which they are needed. (They are helpful in ANY printing session, testing or otherwise.)

STANDARD WHITE. Place a 3-to-4-inch square of unexposed printing paper (same brand and contrast as used for the tests) in the developer for 3 minutes, fix for 5 minutes in fresh hypo and store in fresh water. The Standard White matches for Zone IX.

AGITATION PLANS

In order to keep films from streaking during development, agitation at frequent intervals must be done. Whether such agitation is continuous, at regular or irregular intervals has an effect on the final density in the negative. Therefore to keep contrasts consistent from batch to batch standardized agitation plans must be followed. This is true for either sheet or roll film.

PLAN I *For development times up to* 6 - 7 *minutes.*
Constant agitation—for cut film. For roll film constant agitation for first 15 seconds. Then *one* "tip-over" of the tank every 30 seconds. (continuous agitation causes streaking.)

PLAN II *For development times* 6 - 7 *minutes to* 10 - 12 *minutes.*
Constant agitation for the first minute, 15 seconds agitation every minute thereafter. For roll film, as Plan I.

PLAN III *For development times between* 10 *and* 20 *minutes.*
First minute, constant agitation, 30 seconds agitation *every other* minute thereafter.

PLAN IV *Over* 20 *minutes.*
Follow plan III for first 20 minutes, then 1 minute agitation every fifth minute up to an hour. Occasional agitation thereafter.

THE EYE MATCH METHOD

The various steps of the calibration tests are the same for both roll and sheet film, however the handling of each type is necessarily different. As was said the #2 contrast grade of projection paper is standard with sheet film and the #3 with roll film. The first is chosen because its contrast is midway between the harder and softer contrast grades. The #3 contrast grade is consistent with the general practice for small negatives.

Sheet film can be handled one sheet at a time. Roll film, however, must be both *exposed and processed as entire rolls,* not cut apart in any way. This is necessary because the testing procedure must be as much like customary practice as possible. Testing practice should also become a model for future precision processing, especially with small negatives. Good as daylight tanks and reels are, development is not quite even from end to end of any roll. Consequently the frames specifically for a given test must be exposed in the middle of the roll. Furthermore in order to maintain the chemical action in the test situation as nearly as possible like customary practice, the frames NOT exposed for specific tests must also be exposed to something. The exposure for these "left over" frames is given in the instructions for each test.

STANDARD NEGATIVE PRINTING TIME

1. Develop an *UNexposed s*heet or frame of film according to the time suggested by the manufacturer, or your own customary developing time. (With roll film leave a few frames blank on the roll for the Film Speed Test. With sheet film this unexposed sheet may be developed with the exposed film for the Film Speed Test.)

2. Set the enlarger for an 8 x 10, or a 5 x 7 print, whichever you use the most. *Use that enlargement ratio for all the rest of the tests.* Insert the negative.

3. Set the diaphragm at f/8 or f/11 for a trial run.

4. Make a series of exposures in increments of 2 seconds each on a test strip about 2 inches wide and 10 inches long. This will accommodate ten steps: 2, 4, 6, 8, 10, 12, 14, 16, 18, and 20 seconds. If all the steps come out black after time & temperature processing, reduce the size of the aperture. If all the steps are too light, that is no blacks, increase the size of the aperture. First look, however, for the human errors. Somewhere in the neighborhood of 14 seconds the grey steps should become black ones. This is in the neighborhood of optimum exposure time for many projection papers.

5. Compare the strip with the Standard Black Square while wet. And again after both are dry.

6. The critical step is the last black one beside the first grey step. Take the exposure time of the critical black step as the Standard Negative Printing Time.

Use this SNP time, the f/stop, and the enlargement ratio without fail for all the rest of the calibration tests.

Working Film Speed Test

Tripod the camera and aim it at the 18% neutral test card so that the picture is filled with the image of the target, evenly illuminated by two photofloods in reflectors placed at 45° angles to the target. To avoid reciprocity failure, exposures must not exceed 1 second. The older Weston meters should read a minimum of 13 on target. The equivalent numbers on the Weston Master V and Honeywell Pentax is 8. Set the lens on infinity to insure elimination of texture and the necessity to compensate for bellows extension. *The identical camera and target and illumination set-up must be used for all exposures made in these tests.*

1. EXPOSURE. Set the ASA or DIN film speed rating into the luminance meter.

2. Expose 5 sheets of film to Zone II. Change the film speed numbers for each exposure so that 1 stop less than

78

the recommended Film Speed is given the first sheet; 1/3rd stop less is given the second sheet, ASA or DIN rating for the third, and 1/3rd and 1 stop more for the last two sheets respectively.

Roll Film. Expose 1 roll as follows: Leave a frame or two blank for the first test. "Bracket" the ASA or DIN numbers in thirds of stops, a frame for each, for one or two stops in both directions depending on the number of frames on the roll. Expose the "left over" frames to Zone IX at the rated ASA.

4. PROCESS. Process each roll or sheet for exactly the same number of minutes, time & temperature. Use the manufacturer's recommendations or your own customary time for the particular film-developer combination.

5. PRINTING. Set the enlarger at predetermined height, lens at standardized aperture and give SNP time to each sheet of film. Use 4 x 5 inch sheets of paper even though the enlargement is up to 8 x 10.

Roll Film. Print all the Zone IIs on the roll.

6. MATCHING. Compare these Zone II values to the Standard Black Square, which represents Zone I.

7. The critical or significant negative, roll or sheet, is the one that was exposed for the lowest film speed numbers; the print from which shows a distinct separation from the Zone I black. This number is taken as the new working Film Speed number.

Users of the Zone System rarely change a working film speed once it is found. The number represents a *calibration* of the materials and the equipment, both luminance meter and camera, with his own processing habits. The Working Film Speed is, therefore, respected as a constant.

Normal Development

(5 sheets of film or 5 rolls)

1. EXPOSURE. Set the New Working Film Speed into the meter.

79

2. Expose 5 sheets of film for Zone V.

Roll Film. Expose each of 5 rolls to Zones I, II, III, IV, V, VI, VII, VIII and IX. If 36 exposure rolls happen to be used, make 3 such exposure series on each roll.

3. DEVELOPMENT. Develop each sheet or roll at different times as follows: Recommended or customary time, 10% and 20% less, 10% and 20% more.

4. PRINTING. Expose all of the Zone V negatives at Standard Negative Printing Time. Process Time & Temperature, fix ,wash and dry.

5. MATCHING. Match the Zone V prints to the 18% reflectance target card. Slight differences in color will be bothersome, but not insurmountable.

6. The developing time in minutes of the negative of the matching print is taken as Normal Developing Time.

Roll Film. The Zones II through VIII negatives will be used later for making standard comparison prints, and still later to make a "Value Ruler".

Brightness Range Check

Find a scene out of doors that provides nine consecutive luminance meter readings with texture in both Zone III and VII. Place the 18% grey card prominently in the scene, even if it has to be out of focus. Or set up a corresponding brightness range in the studio with lights and various values and textures.

Make the exposure by placing the reading of the 18% card in Zone V. Give the new Normal Development to the film, and expose and print the resultant negative standard.

The grey card rendering in the print should be within the Zone V series of greys. The rest of the nine areas should be *represented* even if they do not match, and the texture should be obvious in both Zone III and VII.

WRONG RESULTS. If all the values of the entire print are too light or too dark, the camera shutter or the thermometer may be off. But first look over your notes and equipment to locate the personal mistakes. If after checking everything seems all right, adjust the film speed higher or lower to compensate appropriately.

If the texture appears properly in Zone III but is missing in Zone VII, reduce the developing time. If the Zone IX area is a pale grey instead of matching the Standard White Square, increase the development to compensate.

Contrarywise if texture appears in Zone VII but is missing in III, decrease the film speed index.

Expansions (Plus developments)

Used to compensate for brightness ranges of 7 zones or less. Or to stylistically eliminate middle grey values in scenes of normal or very long brightness ranges.

A. COMPARISON STANDARD PRINTS

Comparison standard prints are made at this stage for employment in both expansion and contraction tests.

Sheet Film. Expose one sheet each to Zones III, IV, VI, VII and VIII. Give Normal Development, Standard Negative Print Exposure, Time & Temperature print development. Retain the dry prints for later comparisons.

Roll Film. Make prints as above from the negatives exposed during the Normal test.

B. GENERAL PROCEDURE. To find a starting point for the developing time for expansion of one or more zones a factor of 1.4 is employed. To find the starting point for the N+1 development, the number of minutes found for Normal is multiplied by this 1.4. In just the same way this N+1 time is multiplied by the factor to get the starting point for the N+2. And so on. The multiplied figure is then "bracketed" in 10% increments, more and less than the found figure. The figures are rounded out to the nearest half minutes if the Normal is less than 8 minutes, or to the nearest minute if the Normal is over 10 minutes. It is practical in developing to insert all the sheets into the tank at once and remove each as its specified time is up. A luminous clock dial is imperative to do this, or some one outside the darkroom calling out the minutes.

To save rolls of film, the N+1 and N−1 tests are omitted and the time interpolated between the minutes for Normal and N+2. If one wishes make the plus and minus one test.

Normal + 1

1. Expose 5 sheets to Zone VI.

2. Develop at 5 different times as follows: the Normal development time X 1.4, bracket 10% and 20% less and 10% and 20% more.

3. After processing give the Standard Negative Printing Time to all the negatives.

4. Isolate the print which matches the Zone VII standard Comparison print. The development time of the negative of this print is taken as the Normal +1 zone or N+1.

Normal + 2

Sheet Film

1. Expose 3 sheets of film to Zone VI.

2. Develop each sheet for a different length of time. These times are found by multiplying the N+1 time in minutes by 1.4 and bracketing that number by 20% more or less.

3. Compare prints to the Zone VIII comparison prints.

4. Time of development of the negative of the matching print is taken as the N+2 development time.

Roll Film

1. Expose 5 rolls to Zone VI, all frames.

2. Develop starting with 2 times the Normal development. Bracket 10% and 20% both more and less.

3. Print one frame from each roll. Standard everything.

4. Time of the development of the roll of the print that matches Zone VIII comparison print is taken as the N+2 development time.

5. For N+1 interpolate between Normal and the New N+2.

Normal + 3 and up

The procedures above are followed, only the exposure and matching zones are different. These are given in the chart below.

Development Symbol	Expose to	Develop to Match
N+1	VI	VII
N+2	VI	VIII
N+3	V	VIII
N+4	IV	VIII
N+5	IV	IX

Contractions (Minus Developments)

Contractions are used to compensate for brightness ranges of 9 zones or more, or a drastic reduction in contrast for interpretive purposes.

The major difference in procedure is that the factor of 1.4 is divided into the preceding development time. Bracketing is in the same percentages rounded off to half minutes. A table is given below:

Development Symbol	Expose	For	Develop to Match
N−1	5 sheets	VII	VI
N−2	3 sheets	VIII	VI
N−3	3 sheets	VIII	V
N−4	3 sheets	IX	V

With most film-developer combinations, any contraction of N−2 or more frequently produces muddy negatives. So generally the N−2 development indication is a signal to use the two solution method. For this a 2% Borax solution is used as the second bath to the regular developer for the first bath. The table found in Appendix A will provide the reader with a starting point for his own combination of developer and Borax.

With present day films (1965) one may anticipate that films rated at speeds over 100 will respond to extended development poorly, but well to minus developments. Films with speeds of 100 or less generally respond well to both extended and shortened development times. Ansco's Verapan may be developed as long as N+5 and as little as N—4 with some developers.

Further Brightness Range Checks

Once the tests are finished, the various contraction and expansion times should be validated. Locate scenes or set them up in the studio with appropriate brightness ranges and expose and alter development of the film accordingly. Follow up with the Standardized procedures instead of falling back into the old habits. To check *planned* Zones in prints against what actually appears use a "value ruler".

Making A Value Ruler

Look at Figure 2 or 3 to see how to lay out a "value ruler". Material for each of the zones has already been made. Black Squares will provide Zone I. The Film Speed tests will provide Zone II, the test for Normal Zone V, the Standard White Square Zone IX, and the standard comparison prints will provide the rest.

DO THE TERMS GAMMA AND NORMAL MEAN THE SAME?

The word "Gamma" from photographic sensitometry is not interchangable with "Normal" from the zone system. Gamma stands for the contrast characteristics of a film as determined by the degree of slope of its "straight line portion," and is determined under laboratory conditions. Normal, includes, in order to gain the advantage of the speed of modern films, the "toe portion" of the film's characteristic curve. It is made under field or studio conditons, with one's own equipment and one's personal processing habits. The sin in the latter is inconsistency!

TESTING PROCEDURES WITH A DENSITOMETER

Many students have pointed out that the running and the completion of the calibration tests is akin to an initiation. Perhaps so. Whatever analogy the experience arouses, the testing is undertaken because one chooses to. As we know, we have images of sorts automatically with photography. Willfully choosing to run tests that calibrate a system and a man makes a difference. Hence the truth may be that one is not quite the same person after the calibrations as before. If nothing else, we have an understanding by direct experience of two fundamentals of the medium, what in effect is subject recording and subject rendering.

The testing procedure itself becomes with the doing an intimate part of the zone system and previsualization. Nevertheless the specific methods given here are models. That is, from the understanding of the present method, individual ways of arriving at the same or different standards may be found. The reader must remember that no matter how rigid the testing procedures seem, the underlying concept of previsualization is flexibility itself.

OUTLINE OF METHOD

The *preparations* for testing with a densitometer differ from the preparations for the eye-match method only by the addition of the instrument and learning how to use it.

The 6 fundamental tests retain the same titles. Eye matching is resorted to *in part* for the Standard Negative Printing Time, Working Film Speed and Normal Development Time. Once the Working Film Speed is established, processed, densities read, plotted and characteristic curves drawn, the rest of the test information needed is derived by interpolation. The information is later subjected to Brightness Range Tests.

1. STANDARD NEGATIVE PRINTING TIME   Proceed as described in eye-match method. Then take the density reading of the unexposed & developed negative as Film Base + Fog. This figure may or may not be subtracted from all later density readings, just as you prefer.

2.. WORKING FILM SPEED   For this test follow the directions as given in the first method. When completed make density readings of all Zone II negatives. The Working Film Speed is taken from the negative with the least density the print from which separates Zone I from Zone II distinctly. (Density readings of 0.13 to 0.15 or higher, minus Film Base + Fog, for Zone II densities, may be anticipated with many of today's projection papers.)

3. NORMAL DEVELOPMENT TIME

A. EXPOSURE. Set the Working Film Speed into the meter. Illumination, target and so on are the same as used for the eye-match testing.

Roll Film. Expose 10 rolls of film so that each roll has separate frames exposed to Zones II through XII and a blank for Zone I.

Sheet Film. Out of 20 sheets of film expose 10 sheets to Zones I through VI. Then expose 10 sheets to Zones VII through XII. Instructions follow.

To make several exposures on one sheet of film as required here, employ a multiple exposure method as follows. To make Zone I, push the dark slide into a loaded holder, in the camera, about half an inch, thereby a narrow strip of film is unexposed, while the rest of the sheet is being exposed to Zone II. Then push the dark slide in another half inch, expose the remainder of the sheet by REPEATING the first exposure. So doing gives the exposure for Zone III. Push the dark slide in another half inch. To make the Zone IV exposure, DOUBLE the original exposure. Thereafter change the position of the dark slide with a DOUBLING of the previous exposure to obtain the increase of one zone until Zone VI is completed.

A chart will consolidate these instructions. For the sake of generalization, the information in the chart is given in units of exposure instead of shutter speeds and apertures. The amount of light to produce a Zone II density in the negative is treated as 1 unit of exposure. Zone III requires 2 units, Zone IV 4 units, Zone V requires 8 units and so on in geometrical progression.

For Zone	Give		
I	0 units of light		
II	1 "		
III	1 "		
IV	2 "		1st Series, on each of 10 sheets
V	4 "		
VI	8 "		
VII	32 "		
VIII	32 "		
IX	64 "		
X	128 "		2nd series, on each of 10 sheets
XI	256 "		
XII	512 "		

B. *Development*

3. Place all of the sheet film in a tank of developer at the same time and remove one sheet at a time at increasing intervals starting with ½ the manufacturer's recommended development times up to 3 times that. For example with a recommended time of 8 minutes, remove the first sheet at 4 minutes, the second at 5 minutes and so on as follows, 6, 7, 8, 10, 12, 15, 22, and 30 minutes. Follow the Agitation Plans found on page 76.

Develop roll film at corresponding schedules, one to a few rolls at a time as facilities allow.

C. Plot Curves

When the negatives are dry, read the densities of each frame or step and plot the readings on graph paper. The density figures in logarithms should appear on the left edge of the graph; and the exposure, also in logarithms, on the bottom edge. Connect the readings derived from zones at the identical development times with a line. The resultant curve shows a characteristic of the emulsion-developer combination being tested. This curve is familiarly called the "D Log E" curve in sensitometry. In Figure 11 the exposure numbers along the bottom edge of the graph is stated in Zones. So doing helps the visually minded reader.

The arrangement of the same information that is diagramed in Figure 11 may be presented in another way as seen in Figure 12. The time in minutes are represented by the figures on the bottom edge of the graph, and the curves represent the densities of each zone at different development times.

D. Determination of Normal Development Time

1. Select out of all the Zone Vs, sheet or roll, those the development time of which approach the recommended or customary one, AND the Zone IIs of which have about the same density found earlier to separate Zone I from Zone II on the paper being calibrated in the working film speed test.

2. Print and process these by the same standards used in the eye-match method. Isolate the one that matches the 18% neutral grey target. The development time of the negative the print from which satisfies both the Zone II density requirement and the Zone V match determines Normal Development Time. On the graph the curve associated with this negative is labeled Normal.

4. EDITORIAL DETERMINATION OF EXPANSIONS AND CONTRACTIONS

The various plus and minus development times are determined by means of two controls. The first is the Normal curve and the second is the density in the negative established either at Zone VIII or Zone V. The second is established at the point where the Normal curve and the Vertical Zone VII exposeure line cross, (Figure 11) that is, at the density of a Zone VIII exposure of a Normally developed negative. For visibility a heavy horizontal line is drawn all along the Zone VIII density line.

N+1 To locate the N plus 1 developing time, the Zone VII vertical line is followed up until it cross the heavy horizontal Zone VIII density line. The developing time represented by the D Log E curve that passes through or near this juncture is used as the N+1 development time. This is considered a working or preliminary development time until a brightness range test can be conducted.

N−1 The number of minutes represented by the D Log E curve that passes near or through the junction of the vertical Zone IX line and horizontal Zone VIII line determines the N−1 development time. Interpolate if no curve passes through or near the meeting point. And so on for the rest of the Expansions and Contractions.

If a Zone V density is used for the control density somewhat different numbers of minutes will be given for the various expansions and contractions. Lay a ruler horizontally across the curves in Figure 11 at the Zone V density and check this point. (0.8 in Figure 11.) What zone to use for a control is up to the individual, V or VIII is handy, but there is no reason for not taking VI or VII for control.

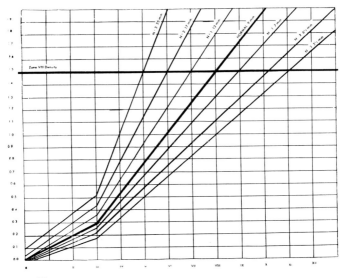

Figure 11

Diagram of development time curves plotted from density readings on a densitometer. The "curves" are highly abstracted and exaggerated. Note that density appears on the left edge of the graph, in logarithms, and exposures in Zones on the bottom edge. The resulting curves indicate development time. From these curves we can see to what extent variable development affects each zone. It is important to realize that the effect is non-linear; that is, there is a greater effect on the denser parts of the negatives, Zone V on up, than on the thin parts, Zone I-III. When the maximum speed of the film is sought, the first three zones are on the "toe portion" of the curve. The change of the curve to the "straight line" portion takes place at about Zone III, or between Zone III and IV. This varies according to film and developer combination.

DETERMINATION OF EXPANSIONS AND CONTRACTIONS

To determine expansion and contractions in zones and minutes a control density is selected. In this illustration the density of Zone VIII was used. (A Zone V density is perhaps even more useful because it is in the middle of the grey scale.) The heavy black line extending horizontally represents the Zone VIII control "line" or density. To find, for example, an N+1 development time, the vertical line of the Zone VII exposure is followed until it crosses the heavy Zone VIII line. The number of minutes of development of the curve (D Log E curve) that passes through or near the meeting point of lines VII and VIII (horizontal line) is considered the working N+1 development time. Later it will be checked with a brightness range test.

90

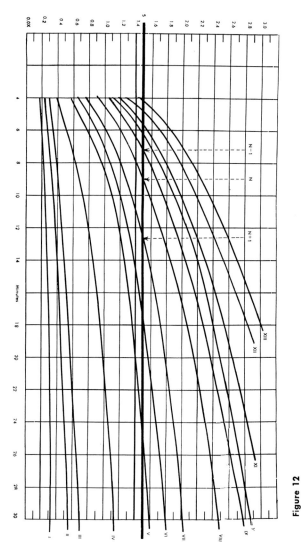

Figure 12

The same information found in Figure 11 is here graphed differently. The time in *minutes* appears along the bottom edge of the graph, and the curves represent the density of each zone at different development times.

91

8. Short Cut Exposure-Development Calculations

To speed up calculations to the "nearly intuitive" point exposure calculations are based on a standard, e.g., one's own hand.

Note: when lighting conditions are unfamiliar or complex, one should employ the positive methods of metering and visualization, upon which these briefer routines are based.

A. TWO READING ROUTINE

1. Take a meter reading of the palm of the hand in shadow, or turned away from the light source.
2. Place this reading in Zone IV to set exposure.
3. Take meter reading of palm of hand in sunlight.
4. Development is determined by the difference in the two readings according to the following table:

For a 5 zone difference give N—2 development.

For a 4 zone difference give N—1 development.

For a 3 zone difference give N   development.

For a 2 zone difference give N+1 development.

For instance if the shadow reading of the hand is placed in Zone IV and the high falls in Zone IX, the difference is 5 zones and according to the table above N—2 development is indicated. The print will render the flesh shadow in Zone IV and the flesh in sunlight in Zone VII. If one prefers flesh in sun rendered in Zone VI an N—3 can be given.

B. ONE READING ROUTINE

1. Development is assumed to be "average" at N—1½.°
2. Read palm of hand in sun.
3. Reading is placed in Zone VII to set exposure.

OR:

1. Read palm of hand in shadow.
2. Place reading in Zone IV to set exposure.

OR:

Place reading of important objects in selected zone to set exposure.

°See Appendix A for explanation of N-1½ for roll film.

9. Previsualization And Photographic Printing Paper

VARIOUS CONTRAST GRADES

Roll film users habitually substitute the various contrast grades of photographic printing paper for variable film development, often without realing that they do so. Consequently few recognize that previsualization of subject rendering according to the various contrast grades of printing paper offers the roll film enthusiast all the advantages of a conscious use of his materials.

Previsualization in terms of the characteristics of photographic paper contrast grades for subject contrast control, by either roll or sheet film is easy enough. First the #2 contrast grade of any given *brand* of projection paper is taken as the norm. Then development of the film is standardized, and called "Normal development time", so that this #2 paper will print a 9 zone subject contrast range in nine steps including Zone I black and Zone IX white. With the Normal print visually and sensitometrically defined the other paper contrast grades exhibit the following relationships:[*]

#1 paper renders a 10 zone subject as a Normal print
#2 paper renders an 9 zone subject as a Normal print
#3 paper renders an 8 zone subject as a Normal print

The next step is the relation between variable development of film and various contrast grades. If a 9 zone subject contrast range is taken to *indicate* Normal, then a 10 zone contrast indicates a N−1 development, and an 8 zone range indicates an N+1 development. We can now chart the correspondence between paper contrast grade and variable development.

[*] The above zonal relationships are generalized for illustration purposes Zonal differences of specific papers may be obtained by empirical testing. Methods are outlined later in the chapter.

8 zone contrast range *indicates* N+1 Normal Development OR #3 paper

9 zone contrast range *indicates* Normal Development OR #2 paper

10 zone contrast range *indicates* N−1 Develompent OR #1 paper

At the period of previsualization alternatives are offered:

N−1 development printed on #2 paper contrast grade

N development printed on #1 paper contrast grade

} 10 zone range

N+1 development printed on #2 paper contrast grade

N development printed on #3 paper contrast grade

} 8 zone range

When fine photographs are concerned the difference in rendering between the alternatives above is noticeable, through subtle. Consequently one makes a choice of the alternatives only after an intimate knowledge has been learned of the nature of the materials and processes actually employed in camera and darkroom.

COMBINATIONS OF VARIABLE DEVELOPMENT AND VARIOUS PAPER CONTRAST GRADES

Variable film development may be combined with various contrast paper grades, in a kind of "additive" manner. For example a 5 zone subject contrast range is to be dealt with. After *placement* of the Shadow in Zone III, which accounts for 3 zones the highlight reading *falls* in Zone V. With appropriate increased development the Zone V area, which with Normal development would be rendered in Zone V, could be *developed to* a Zone VII − actually an N+2 development of the film. Next, if the #3 paper contrast grade were used instead of the #2, the area in question would be rendered in Zone VIII. So the effect of an

N+3 development may be obtained by a combination of an N+2 development combined with printing on #3 paper instead of #2.

CHART FOR SUBJECT CONTRAST CONTROL
(The arbitrary divisions below refer to subject contrast ranges counted in zones.)

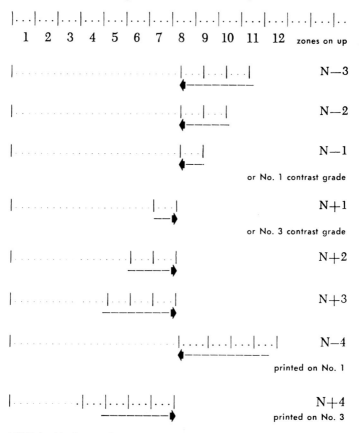

NOTE: In this chart an 8-zone contrast range is used as the point of departure. With the various paper grades, any one development time for a roll of film can be compensated for 3 different exposure ranges.

ROLL FILM AND VARIABLE DEVELOPMENT

As has been said variable film development is just as applicable to roll film as sheet. *One simply has to keep the various subject contrast ranges included on each roll within the limits of what the various paper contrast grades can handle.* As has been pointed out the various papers can handle about three different contrast ranges. *If these bounds are exceeded, willfully or accidentally, some frames on a roll must be sacrificed.*

For example buildings on the shady side of the street offer a general series of contrast ranges of 6 zones. To obtain Normal prints a N+2 is indicated. Any contrast range of 5 zones, or 6 zones, or 7 zones included on one roll may be rendered as Normal prints by giving the whole roll N+2 development and print the shorter contrast range on 3# paper, the middle range on #2 paper and the longer range on #1.

Examples in which the the contrast ranges require Minus development can also be handled with the appropriate less development and the various paper contrast grades.

EMPIRICAL TESTS

To determine the *actual* differences from grade to grade of the brand of paper that you expect to, or use, some empirical tests are necessary. A workable method follows:

1. Find or make a "Normal" negative all the different value areas of which are big enough to be compared *easily* by a "value ruler" on an 8 x 10 print. (Choose a negative that has produced a full-scale print in the past).

2. Print the negative on a #2 projection photographic paper of your choice adjusting the exposure so the light areas show textures and substance in either Zone VIII or VII. Determine precisely which.

3. Print the same negative on a #3 projection paper of the same brand, and also on a #1 paper. In each case

adjust the exposure so that the *light area* is rendered *identically* in all three prints.

4. Compare the shadow areas.

   If by some good fortune the proper negative has been chosen:

   A. The print from the #2 paper will show detail in the shadows and also Zones I to IX. Moving a "value ruler" around the print will make it possible to check whether or not every zone is present.

   B. Next take the print from the #3 paper and check zones with the value ruler. What was rendered in Zone IV on the #2 print will probably be rendered in Zone III on this print. If so, then one has a visual demonstration of whatever difference there is between a #2 and a #3 contrast grade paper. The difference may be as much as one Zone as measured on the value ruler.

   C. Do the same for the print from the #1 paper. This may show no black Zone I at all.

Filters for the variable contrast papers may be compared in the same way. Generally each consecutive filter is about a half a zone difference in contrast. This is not consistent throughout a whole set of filters, and so should be tested carefully.

Occasionally boxes of variable contrast paper will be found that do not respond properly to one end or the other of the filter series.

10. Previsualization and the Development of Intuition

Photography serves all kinds of image-making talent in mankind with an equality that almost amounts to an holy indifference. It does not distinguish the sleeper from the transcendentalist; it serves the first with its automatic mechanicalness, the second with its power to evoke the sense of light in images. It gives the spark of creativity in anyone a fine chance to grow. And from those people who have grown to love photography and master it have come three psychological concepts: Equivalence (Alfred Stieglitz), Previsualization (Edward Weston and Ansel Adams), and Response. (The latter sometimes goes under the name of "reading photographs".) These concepts give affirmation to individuals who pursue consciousness and wakefulness by way of photography.

The subject of this manual is obviously Previsualization and only the briefest hints have been dropped that the other concepts exist, and nothing at all of how the three are intimately interdependent. This chapter will do no more than point out that previsualization can be extended to include composition, design, memory of former images, metaphor and the prediction of audience response, all disciplines which may become intuitive.

But one more point first. No one has to learn to previsualize or learn to use the zone system who does not want to, or who does not wish to. The significance of the whole matter lies in just that opportunity of choice. Photography will give anyone some kind of an image; to choose to previsualize even with every exposure, must always be the man's own decision. The camera machine is made for those who are satisfied to let everything happen to them. Previsualizations requires an effort, an act of will, therefore relates man to some form of higher "do".

Previsualization as a practice is easy to extend from work with subject and print values to design. The camera frame isolates a composition every time; one can learn to see the same *before* the camera gets to the eye. A quote from Ansel Adams on page 102 expands the point.

The act of mentally superimposing an imagined image on a present scene requires an active effort of a special kind. The quotation from Henri Bergson on page 103 touches on the specialness of the act. Furthermore there is a direct connection between previsualization and the use and function of camera images as metaphors, or the creative concept of Equivalence. The act of seeing "meaning" within a print is little or no different than seeing the print within the scene.

A certain degree of creativeness is required to establish a rapport with the image in a scene or on the groundglass. This creativeness relates to the photographer. An equal degree of creativeness is necessary on the part of the audience to be receptive enough to get the import and content of a photograph. In photography there is a common bond of creativeness between the photographer and his responsive audience. With training the photographer can learn to previsualize audience responses. With training the audience can learn to visualize, so to speak, backwards to the meanings of the photographer, whatever he meant as a human being at the period of exposure.

The common creativeness of photographer and audience lies in the reality when "Contact" or rapport is established with the "meaning" of the print, on the part of the audience, and with the subject to be photographed on the part of the photographer. The creativeness in both instances lies in "creating" an openess in themselves. This is as much as any man can do. The rest is grace.

EXTEND PREVISUALIZATION
UNTIL THE NEGATIVE IMAGE BELOW
CAN BE SEEN IN YOUR OWN EYE

In a manual we have to substitute a photograph for the original scene, and for a person visualizing on location. What is actually meant here is to previsualize the negative image of the positive scene on the spot. Such is a further exercise leading to intuition. Notice that the picture has been rotated; such rotation is mentally possible during the concentration necessary to previsualize.

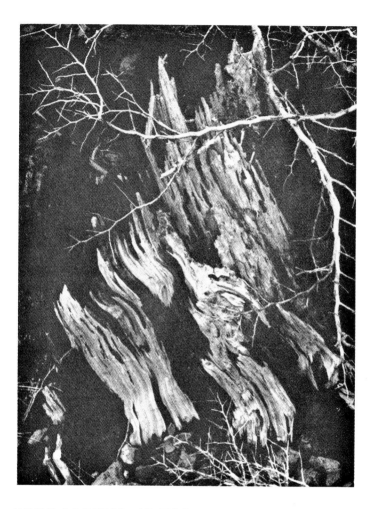

WHILE LOOKING AT THIS

PREVISUALIZATION AND DESIGN

Regarding one's earliest encounters with previsualization Ansel Adams says *(Basic Photo Series, Book, IV, p. 36):*

"A technique difficult for any photographer to master is the visualization of various colors in terms of black-and-white tonalities. The classic example is the red apple on the green leaf; the panchromatic film records both of these values in the *same shade of gray.* It may not be emotionally or even representationally adequate. This does not concern the photometricist, but it profoundly concerns the practical photographer. His problem is to obtain an image that is an adequate visual and/or emotional statement. He may visualize certain tones in the print that are not photometrically accurate.

"...But the ability to actually obtain these tones in the image, through use of filters and control of exposure and development, is the mark of an artist who has mastered his medium."

On page 15 of the same book he refers to the inter-influence of design — and previsualization:

"The element of design — photographic design — is of extreme importance in visualizing the image. Great enthusiasm for the subject sometimes veils a clear concept of the image of it! An exciting subject, such as a cluster of fine farm buildings, may exist in an enviroment of space of field and sky, but in the print this "space" may appear as dull, neutral areas of distressingly low interest. Space in nature is one thing: space confined and restricted by the picture edges is quite another thing. Space and forms must be made eloquent — not in imitation of ordinary painting arrangements...but in terms of the living camera image. Design, form, tone, and texture must all be considered together in a sensitive visualization of a photograph."

TO STILL FURTHER EXTEND PREVISUALIZATION
LOOK AT THESE LETTERS JUXTAPOSED

 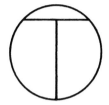

AND IMAGINE THEM SUPERIMPOSED

"X" beside "T" does little but "X" on top of "T" visually explodes. "K", "V", Pi, hourglass, Da Vinci's Man, etc. . .

Henri Bergson, French philosopher (1859-1941), gives, what amounts to a recipe for strengthening intuition (Gestalt-free vision in terms of the depth psychologist): to mentally superimpose visual objects. He describes what goes on thus:

"When I direct my attention inward to contemplate my own self...I perceive at first, as a crust solidified on the surface, all the perceptions which come to it from the material world. These perceptions are clear, distinct, juxtaposed or juxtaposable one with another; they tend to group themselves into objects...But if I draw myself in from the periphery towards the center...I find an altogether different thing. There is beneath these sharply cut crystals and this frozen surface, a continuous flux which is not comparable to any flux I have ever seen. There is a succession of states each of which announces that which follows and contains that which precedes it. In reality no one begins or ends, but all extend into each other."

IMAGINE JUXTAPOSED IMAGES

The depth psychologist claims that juxtaposed objects concern the pattern-making Gestalt of the surface mind, but not the Gestalt-free depth mind. For this superimposition is both tool and garden. (Again the illustrations are at best symbols of a person actually looking at crystalline clear objects and imagining wall and man's face interweaving in a dance of superimposition.)

104

AS SUPERIMPOSED

Not all persons will be able to literally see two juxtaposed images "move together" and overlap each other. For that matter not everyone interested in doing so can see in his own eye a "tone-seen" actually transform itself into a "tone-imagined." Such persons are not denied the practical advantages of the zone system, nor the planning of interpretations.

11. Appendices

Two Solution Developer For Contractions

(Applies to either sheet or roll film.)

A two-solution developer is advantageous because it favors the low exposure zones I, II and III when excessive contractions are given, N−2 or more. With such a developer the low zones attain their usual density in the negative while the high zones X, XI, and over are readily brought to the required Zone VIII printing density. An all-metol developer seems best followed by a second bath of borax. The formulas:

```
FIRST BATH: D-23
    Water (125° F.)    .    .    .    .    .    .    750.0 cc.
    Metol  .    .    .    .    .    .    .    .    .      7.5 g.
    Sodium Sulphite .    .    .    .    .    .    .    100.0 g.
    Water to make  .    .    .    .    .    .    .    1000.00 cc. (1 liter)

SECOND BATH: 2% Solution of Borax
    Water (125° F.) .    .    .    .    .    .    .    100.0 cc.
    Borax (granular) .    .    .    .    .    .    .     20.0 g.
    Water to make  .    .    .    .    .    .    .    1000.0 cc. (1 liter)
```

The brightness ranges are controlled by the number of minutes the film remains in the first bath. The second bath speeds up development so that whatever developer is in contact with silver grains is exhausted. In the dense areas the available developer is used up before the grains are fully developed. In the thin areas there is more developer available in proportion to the developable grains so that most of them are fully developed. Consequently the density in the low zones reaches normal printing density while the upper zones are vigorously controlled.

The chart of suggested development times on the next page will not apply to all films but will serve as a starting point.

Development Symbol	D-23	2% Borax
N	7 minutes	3 minutes
N — 1	6 "	3 "
N — 2	5 "	3 "
N — 3	4 "	3 "
N — 4 to 5	3 "	3 "

NOTE: Expanded developments are not recommended with this developer. Constant agitation is required in the first bath and for the first two minutes in the Borax bath.

To take full advantage of the two-solution developers for roll film "exposure by the roll" is recommended. Otherwise the ubiquitous multi-contrast rolls "average" development time of less than Normal is ideal. Obviously a development time that will allow the greatest number of brightness ranges to be controlled is highly desirable. An N—1 or preferably an N—1½ was found to give maximum control when combined with the printing variables: approximately from a 6 zone brightness range to a 12 zone brightness range. For example, with a 12 zone brightness range the N—1½ development brings the contrast in the negative to about 10½ zones which can be printed nearly full scale on a No. 1 projection in an Extra Soft developer.

Furthermore the reduced development time aids in keeping the grain at a minimum. For roll-film, development at a constant temperature of 68° in developer, Borax bath, short stop, fresh hypo and wash water is highly recommended to keep grain at a minimum.

APPENDIX B

ARCHIVAL PHOTOGRAPHY FOR MAXIMUM PERMANENCE

Maximum permanence of photographs concerns many photographers and all collectors, private or museum. History is a part of it, but permanence is also a large factor in the selling price of fine photographs. And the fact that photographs are notoriously fragile and subject to stains from sulfur in air, and mount stock is one of the reasons why they never command the investment prices of graphic prints.

Maximum permanence of photographs requires a combination of optimal processing AND special storage-exhibition conditions. Archivally processed photographs dry mounted on sulfur-bearing mount stock does not lead to maximum permanence. On this whole subject the thinking of photographers and collectors is due for a change. We need to conclude that Exhibition prints are expendable and only Archival photographs require permanence. In the galleries this means that collectors could have a choice between Exhibition prints and Archival prints. The price difference could be substantial. The collector can hang the exhibition-mounted photographs on his walls, store them carelessly in his cabinets and lend them for shows. If no accidental physical damage occurs the prints may last 20 to 30 years. The collector must handle and store the Archival print in the special way given in detail below. The life expectancy of the prints approaches a century or more, though no one is positive on this point yet.

Archival Photography Has Several Features

1. Optimum development of the print; neither underdevelopment, nor over-development. This prevents processing stains that appear years later.
2. 3% Acetic Acid short stop bath.
3. Fresh hypo-hardner treatment for no more than 5 *minutes*.
4. Selenium toning for protective purposes, not color change.
   A. Prints stored in running water till ready to tone.
   B. Fresh Plain Hypo bath (*no hardener*) at 70 degrees. (32 oz. dry measure, Hypo Crystals. Add water to make one gallon.) **5 minutes**
   C. Do not rinse in water but put directly into.
   D. Selenium Toner at 80 degrees F. *5 minutes*.
   (3 oz. Perma-Wash to 1 gallon water. Add 100-200cc Kodak Rapid Selenium Toner. Or, same amount Toner to one gallon of Working Solution, Kodak Hypo Clearing Agent.)

Tone until the "green" color is replaced by a very faint bluish or purplish tinge. This gives a selenium metal protective coating to the silver grains which are tarnished by sulfur. The contrast of the print will be slightly increased.

5. Wash in running water at 70 degrees. *5 minutes.*

6. Edwal Perma-Wash working solution (70 degrees) OR Kodak Hypo eliminator working solution. *5 minutes.*

7. Last wash — running water, 70 degrees, for 15 minutes minimum. Have washer checked for water change efficiency. A total change of water every 3 minutes is desirable. Washing by hand with water changes of one minute each is often the best.

1. Images printed with minimum of one inch borders on all 4 sides.

2. Cropped on the easel exactly as wanted.

3. Images stored *untrimmed,* and displayed *untrimmed* beneath overmats. This is to protect the edges of the print from chipping, and to prevent air stains from attacking the edges of the images.

Archival Cropping And Trimming

The cause of fading and staining is sulfur; in the air, in mount stock, and in contact with sulfur bearing papers.

1. Buy and cut to standard mount sizes several sheets of 100% rag unbleached, 4 ply Museum Board. (Only a few special paper companies handle it.)

2. Attach Archival photograph to mount by a tape hinge, top or side (Dennison Holland tape).

3. Cover with a cut-out overmat, of the same Museum Board, the "window" is the same or slightly larger in size than the image.

4. Hinge the overmat at top to the undermat by the Holland tape.

5. To further protect the print from abrasion a sheet (a little smaller than the mount) of Strathmore Natural Art Parchment, sulfur-free, is placed between the overmat and print.

Dry mount tissue is inert and "seals" the print from the sulfur-bearing undermat. When the photographs are stored in piles, unfortunately, we can not use dry mount tissue on the surface of the print to isolate it from the mount on top.

By not dry mounting the prints, if stains should occur later, the print can sometimes be restored by appropriate chemical processing. Permanently mounted prints prevent or hinder such restoration.

Archival Mounting

Store in all-rag paper lined print boxes in dust proof cabinets.

The archival prints can be studied in their storage mats in a room set aside for the purpose.

Table for Reciprocity Failure Compensations

When light levels drop below a certain intensity photographic emulsions fail to respond in the customary manner. Consequently compensation is required when indicated exposures (including the working aperture) are a second or longer.

If the indicated exposure is							
If the indicated exposure is			1 second,	increase exposure by		1¼	times
"	"	"	5 seconds,	"	"	1½	"
"	"	"	15 seconds,	"	"	2	"
"	"	"	45 seconds,	"	"	2½	"
"	"	"	2 minutes,	"	"	3	"
"	"	"	5 minutes,	"	"	4	"
"	"	"	10 minutes,	"	"	5	"
"	"	"	20 minutes,	"	"	6	"
"	"	"	40 minutes,	"	"	8	"

This table from Dunn is in use by the Freshman class at Rochester Institute of Technology.

The Dr. Beer's formulas:

SOLUTION A

Water (at 125° F.)	750	cc.
Metol (or Elon)	8	g.
Sodium Sulphite	23	g.
Sodium Carbonate	24	g.
Potassium Bromide	1.1	g.
Water to make	1000	cc. (1 liter)

SOLUTION B

Water (at 125° F.)	800	cc.
Hydroquinone	8	g.
Sodium Sulphite	23	g.
Sodium Carbonate	32	g.
Potassium Bromide	2.2	g.
Water to make	1000	cc.

MIXTURE RATIOS

	Extra Soft	Medium	Extra Hard
Solution A . . .	1 part	1 part	1 part
Solution B . . .	none	1 part	7 parts
Water	1 part	1 part	none

Full development for most projection papers is from about 3 minutes for Extra Soft to 1½ minutes for the Extra Hard. Solutions A and B can be mixed in other proportions to gain a refinement for paper contrast control.

Paste on Zone Scales

Weston Master III

Honeywell Pentax
Mekano Spotron
and other tubular
models.

Attach with the Zone V
covering the arrow on
the meters, or the red
dot, or whatever means
is used to indicate the
calibrated setting.

Weston Master V

Weston Master IV

The recent Weston Ranger 9 Exposure Meter has a Ansel Adams Zone System calculator as optional choice of calculator dials. The presence of the print value scale marked in zones, plus a candles-per-square-foot dial, makes this meter one of the most useful of all luminance meters for planned photography. In addition the physical size of the meter is masculine and big enough to make the dials readable and full of information. The 18 degree angle of the light sensitive cell makes the meter still more useful.

Special reprints on adhesive-backed paper of page 111 are available at 50 cents each from Morgan & Morgan, Inc., 400 Warburton Ave., Hastings-on-Hudson, N. Y. 10706.

The Captive Voice

The Captive Voice

B. J. Hoff

Tyndale House Publishers, Inc.
WHEATON, ILLINOIS

Published in 1987 as *The Domino Image* by Accent Books

Scripture quotations are taken from the *Holy Bible,* New International Version®. Copyright
1973, 1978, 1984 by International Bible Society. Used by permission of Zondervan Publishing
House. All rights reserved. The "NIV" and "New International Version" trademarks are registered in the United States Patent and Trademark Office by International Bible Society. Use of
either trademark requires permission of International Bible Society.

Library of Congress Cataloging-in-Publication Data

Hoff, B. J. (Brenda Jane)
  [Domino image]
  The captive voice / B. J. Hoff.
    p. cm. — (Daybreak mysteries ; 2)
  Previously published: The domino image. Elgin, Ill. : Accent Books, 1987.
  ISBN 0-8423-7193-1 (softcover)
  I. Title. II. Series: Hoff, B. J. (Brenda Jane). Daybreak mysteries ; 2.
  PS3558.034395D66 1996
  813'.54—dc20   96-12927

Printed in the United States of America

01 00 99 98 97 96
7   6   5   4   3   2   1

AUTHOR'S NOTE

My sincere thanks to Cedar Point Marketing Department Sandusky, Ohio, for questions so graciously answered and information so generously supplied.

Crowds may praise
And nations cheer,
The whole world may applaud . . .
But above the noise,
His own will hear
The still, small voice of God.

B. J. Hoff
From "Voices"

The man on the beach tugged at the zipper of his navy jacket, then shoved his hands into the pockets of his jeans. He stared for a moment more at the small dollhouse-like cottage he had been watching for over an hour, then turned and walked away.

She hadn't come out of the cottage tonight. Last night and the evening before, she had gone walking. But not tonight. He could see a soft glow of light behind the drapes, and once the door had opened just enough to admit a small gray-and-white cat. But he hadn't caught even a glimpse of her before she disappeared behind the closed door.

The man stopped walking and looked toward the pier. His gaze fastened on the white lighthouse just beyond, its red light blinking through the gathering dusk. The air off Lake Erie was damp, unusually cool for July.

After a few seconds he ran a hand through his hair, passed it over the back of his neck, then resumed his long-legged, uneven stride. He hurried down a narrow lane between two rows of cottages, crossed an alley, and turned into a dark, isolated street. Unlocking the door of a dusty black car, he glanced around, then quickly slid behind the steering wheel, his head brushing the roof of the car. He punched the key into the ignition and immediately pressed the power door lock. His hands trembled slightly on the steering wheel as he waited for the engine to warm up.

He glanced at his watch, then pulled a small penlight from the glove compartment. Focusing a stream of light on the seat beside him, he flipped through the pages of a black ring binder until he found what he wanted. He stared for a long time at a newspaper photo beneath a transparent sheet protector. Finally his gaze moved to the article beneath the picture. Lowering the penlight, he scanned the brief article, clipped from the *Nashville Banner* three years earlier.

Vali Tremayne continues to be unavailable for comment regarding her career plans. The top female vocalist in the contemporary Christian music industry for over two years, Miss Tremayne is said to be recovering from an emotional collapse following the recent tragic death of her fiancé, composer and recording artist Paul Alexander, in an airplane crash over the Appalachian Mountains.

Joanne Seldon, Miss Tremayne's agent, has also refused to discuss her client's future plans. Sources say, however, that Miss Tremayne has "retired" from the music industry and is presently recuperating at a lakefront resort in northern Ohio, near the family of Paul Alexander.

The deceased musician's mother, renowned novelist and literary award winner Leda Alexander, resides in Sandusky, Ohio. His twin brother, Dr. Graham Alexander, is a well-known and highly respected research scientist who founded Alexander Center, one of the largest and most influential research centers in the country. The Center is located in northern Ohio, and Dr. Alexander makes his home in Port Clinton. . . .

The man looked up from the news article and pushed a cassette tape into the car player. For several moments he sat unmoving, staring straight ahead, his fingers on the steering wheel drumming a mindless accompaniment to the rich female voice on the tape.

He finally switched off the penlight and eased out of the parking place, then turned up the volume on the voice of Vali Tremayne.

Vali had seen him again tonight. Or at least she thought she had. This was the third straight evening she had felt as if someone was watching her, waiting. But whenever she looked for him, she saw little more than a vague silhouette beyond the seawall.

A shadow, that's all it was. She wouldn't bother Graham with it. There was no need to raise more questions. . . .

With an uneasy frown, she dropped the corner of the drapes and turned from the window. Her gaze swept the living room, usually a cheerful splash of color with its lemon walls and floral chintz, but now steeped in shadows from the dim light of a table lamp. After a moment, she walked across the room and picked up a framed photograph from the bookshelf. A dark-haired man laughed out at her. Gently, she touched the glass with her index finger, rubbing the surface as if she could evoke a response. *Paul* . . .

Almost guiltily, she set the frame back in place. Graham had wanted her to put his brother's photograph away long ago. At first, he had only suggested that she remove this last memento of her relationship with Paul. Later, suggestion had strengthened to request, but even though Vali was reluctant to hurt Graham, she couldn't bring herself to let go of this last image of the man she had loved with all her heart.

She stood staring at the photo, remembering the day it had been taken. Paul had laughed about his agent's insistence that he should adopt a more serious, thoughtful expression for his publicity photos. . . .

"I'm supposed to look more—*intense*," he had told Vali, drawing his face into a ridiculous caricature of stern piety. The expression lasted only a second before he broke into his irrepressible grin.

Paul, with his laughing heart and smiling eyes . . . always so happy, so confident, so hopeful. Until all the bright and wonderful things that endeared him were destroyed in a burning plane.

Vali pressed the fingertips of one hand to her temple, where a subtle pulse of pain was beginning to throb. It was always that way when she let herself remember, when she allowed her thoughts to drift back to the time they'd had together, the things they had shared. . . .

No. Don't try to remember. Graham was right. She mustn't think about the past. She mustn't try to remember. Yesterday was dead. It was meant to be buried. Buried with Paul.

Reluctantly she turned away from the photograph and went back to the window, again nudging a corner of the drapes aside to look out. No one was there.

At last she turned and after checking the locks on both the front and back doors, took her pill, then settled down on the couch to read Leda Alexander's latest novel.

O H, Daniel—I wish you could see the beach! It looks exactly the way I remember it." Jennifer tugged at Dan's hand to pull him along beside her, then stopped to allow Sunny, Dan's golden retriever guide dog, to do her job.

Her husband of exactly one week smiled at her excitement. "I'll see it through your eyes, love. But let me take off my shoes first, OK? I never could walk in sand with my shoes on."

Jennifer plopped down beside him on the warm sand and pulled off her own tennis shoes, then sat looking out over Lake Erie. Even though it was warm for September, the beach was dotted with only a few people. The Labor Day weekend was over, bringing an end to the annual vacation season. The few tenants and cottage owners still in the area would now be occupied with readying their cottages for winter. Most of them would be gone by the end of the month.

"Glad we came?" Dan asked, pulling her to her feet with one hand.

"It means the world to me," Jennifer said, her voice soft. "The Smokies were wonderful, but this place is so special to me, Daniel. My family brought us up here every summer until the year before Mother died." She took his tennis shoes and carried them with her own so he could hold Sunny's harness and still walk arm in arm with her.

1

"There's a pier not too far away from us—with a lighthouse at the end," she told him. "When I was a kid, I used to fish there with my dad."

It was second nature for her to help Dan see things through her eyes. Several months ago, he had hired her as his executive assistant at the Christian radio station he owned in West Virginia. By now Jennifer had grown accustomed to keeping up a continual flow of observation so Dan would always be aware of his surroundings.

He had been blind for more than five years. But in spite of his disability, Dan was the most fascinating, and often the most baffling, man Jennifer had ever met. He was almost overwhelming in size. He topped Jennifer's five-eight by more than half a foot, and he had the athletic physique of a former Olympic swimming champion. Yet he was easily the gentlest, kindest man she had ever known.

In Jennifer's eyes, her husband was a remarkable man—and she loved him more than life. She flooded Dan's world with affection, and he, in turn, openly adored her, cherished her, and made her— she was certain—the happiest woman on earth.

She was also an acutely *curious* woman. At the sight of a sprawling stone bi-level house standing at least a hundred yards away from its nearest neighbor, Jennifer came to an abrupt halt. The house was secluded almost to the point of obscurity by enormous trees and a high seawall. Nevertheless, it presented a friendly, inviting appearance, with early fall flowers blooming all across the front and pale yellow curtains blowing at the open windows.

"I've *got* to get a closer look at this place!" she said, abruptly tugging at Dan's arm. "Come on, Daniel."

"Jennifer, don't—" Too late, Dan swerved, the retriever stopped, and Jennifer whirled around to correct her mistake. All three collided.

"Uh-oh," Jennifer muttered, looking up at Dan's face. "I did it again, didn't I?"

Dan's reply was an exaggerated wince of pain as he gingerly touched one rib.

Immediately concerned, Jennifer drew in a sharp breath of dismay. "Did I *hurt* you? Oh, Daniel, I'm *sorry!* I wasn't thinking—I was staring at this wonderful house! I'm *really* sorry. . . ."

As if he could no longer contain it, he flashed a roguish grin. "That's OK, darlin'," he said mildly. "I don't suppose I can complain about your running into me when that's what brought us together in the first place."

Jennifer gave the afflicted rib a gentle shove. "I didn't run into *you* that day, Daniel Kaine. You ran into *me.*"

Still grinning, he shrugged. "Whatever. It worked."

"Come *on*, Daniel! I want to get a closer look at this house."

"What's so great about it?" he asked, looking a little disgruntled at being led by both his wife and his dog. He stumbled over a stone and stopped where he was. "If you two are going to work as a team, I wish you'd get your act together."

"This place is *not* your typical lakeside cottage," Jennifer said distractedly, urging him on. "It's all stone, and it goes on forever. And it's so mysterious looking."

"Mysterious looking," Dan repeated dryly. "What's that mean?"

Slowing her stride, Jennifer gripped his arm a little tighter, then started up a narrow walkway that led from the end of the seawall to the front door of the house. "It has a certain . . . presence," she told him. "It looks like a house with secrets."

When Dan mumbled something inaudible, Jennifer ignored him and kept on going.

She started toward the side of the house, but Daniel hesitated. "Do you hear that?" he said, stopping to listen.

The sound of music came pouring from the house. It sounded like a full-sized band, but Jennifer recognized a state-of-the-art keyboard when she heard one. She also knew enough music to spot the technique of a professional.

"It's coming from this side of the house," Jennifer said, abruptly leading off to the right. "Let's go around where we can hear better."

Dan dug in his heels. "Jennifer . . . am I right in assuming that we're tramping around on private property?"

Jennifer looked at him. "We're not going to bother anyone, Daniel." Again she tried to get him to move. This time Sunny gave Jennifer a look of mild exasperation as if to convey the point that she needed no help in doing her job.

Dan sighed but resumed walking. "I'm totally dominated by two females."

"And you love it. Now come on."

A large casement window was open at the front of the house, and Jennifer headed resolutely toward it. They stopped only a few feet away. The brilliantly executed instrumental music reverberating from the house was now joined by an incredibly smooth, powerful female voice—a voice with tremendous range and perfect control.

Dan reached for Jennifer's hand and squeezed it as they stood listening.

It was a wonderful song, the lyrics a powerful testimony to the grace and glory of God. And Jennifer had never heard it before. Within the course of a week's broadcasting at the station, she heard all the current CCM pop and traditional chart-toppers, as well as any promising new recordings. If this song had been out there, she would have known it. This one was brand new, she was sure—and a natural hit.

But it wasn't only the song that held her captive. It was the voice.

Dan, too, seemed riveted by the singer. "Jennifer . . . do you recognize that voice?" he asked in a low murmur.

"I know I should; it's awfully familiar. . . ." Jennifer drew in a sudden sharp breath. *"Daniel* . . . that almost sounds like . . . but, no, it couldn't be—"

"Tremayne," Dan said softly, shaking his head in wonder. "Vali Tremayne. It has to be her."

"But it *can't* be," Jennifer protested stubbornly. "Vali Tremayne hasn't sung for years. Besides, what in the world would she be doing up here?"

"I think Paul Alexander was from somewhere in this area. Wasn't there some speculation after he died that Vali Tremayne came up here to live so she could be close to his family?"

"I don't remember anything like that. But I *do* remember that she quit singing."

"I'm telling you, that's her," Dan insisted.

Jennifer knew it was unlikely that he was mistaken. Still, she found it difficult, if not impossible, to believe that they were standing outside a beach house listening to one of the Christian music industry's most popular singers.

A thought struck Jennifer. "Didn't Vali Tremayne have some sort of nervous breakdown after Paul Alexander was killed?"

Dan was paying far more attention to the music than to Jennifer. He nodded vaguely. "I heard something like that, but . . ." He paused. "Weird . . ."

"Weird? What's weird?"

He shook his head. "Nothing. It was just a feeling I had for a minute. Listen to that keyboard. Someone sure knows their stuff, huh?"

"Well, I'm going to find out who's in there," Jennifer said briskly.

"Jennifer, we can't just go to the door."

Jennifer was already moving toward the front of the house. "Of course we can, Daniel," she said. "Don't worry, I won't embarrass you. We'll simply introduce ourselves and find out who—"

Her voice faltered, then caught. She stopped dead when she

saw the front door open. *"Daniel—,"* she hissed furtively—"somebody's coming out! Let's go back around to the side so they won't think we're snooping."

"We *are* snooping, Jennifer," Dan said testily. "Where are you, anyway?"

"Wait!" Jennifer caught his arm, restraining him while she peered around the corner of the house.

The man stepping off the small concrete porch into the yard was tall—nearly as tall as Daniel, Jennifer thought. And like Daniel, he also wore a beard, though his was more closely trimmed. There, however, the resemblance ended.

Where Daniel's frame was powerful and muscled from years of disciplined training as a swimmer, this man looked lean and wiry, almost gaunt. His hair was an odd tawny shade, generously threaded with silver—in direct contrast to his darker beard. His skin was deeply tanned, and as he walked out into the yard Jennifer could see that he had a slight but noticeable limp, as if his right leg were somewhat stiff.

It was his voice, however, that made her eyes widen with curiosity. He spoke in a hoarse, strained whisper as he turned to the open doorway.

"Vali, I don't see her anywhere. Maybe we'd better go look."

Both Jennifer and Daniel jumped, reacting not only to the strange whisper of the voice but to the name the voice had spoken. Jennifer's eyes followed the direction of the stranger's gaze, and she expelled a soft sound of amazement.

Framed in the doorway of the house stood a slight young woman with a lovely patrician face, a face as familiar to most Christian music fans as her voice.

Too stunned with excitement to be discreet, she blurted out, "Dan—it's *her!* It's Vali Tremayne!" She flushed with embarrassment as both the woman in the doorway and the light-haired man whirled around in surprise.

TWO

U H . . . hello," Jennifer stammered weakly, feeling decidedly foolish.

There was no reply. Vali Tremayne's expression wasn't hostile, only curious. But the man appraised the Kaines with a speculative, none-too-friendly stare that added a touch of uneasiness to Jennifer's embarrassment.

Obviously, the present circumstances called for an explanation. Just as obviously, Daniel had no intention of offering that explanation.

"We were just . . . uh . . . taking a walk." Jennifer paused, waited, and tried again. "I noticed your house and wanted to get a closer look at it. There aren't many places along the beach nearly as nice as this. . . . That's why it caught my attention. You see, I used to come up here all the time with my family, so I remember things pretty well. But I can't remember seeing this place before."

The blond man's skeptical stare unnerved Jennifer as much as Daniel's deliberate silence irritated her. Her words spilled out even faster. "I was telling Daniel—this is Daniel—," she explained, tugging at his arm to coax him closer, "how attractive your home is. Oh, by the way, I'm Jennifer Terry. I mean, Jennifer *Kaine*. We're on our honeymoon, you see. We've been married a week now."

She glanced at Daniel and saw that he appeared to be cringing.

"I'm terribly sorry," she said, determined to redeem herself. She felt a flicker of hope when a ghost of a smile touched Vali Tremayne's lips. "I suppose you think we're trespassing—actually, we *are* trespassing, I know. But we couldn't resist your music. Daniel owns a radio station—a Christian station—and he recognized your voice, Miss Tremayne. I told him it couldn't be you, but . . ."

"Jennifer . . ." Daniel's voice was pleasantly soft, unmistakably firm, and enormously welcome. Jennifer breathed a long sigh of relief. He would take charge now. She smiled at Vali Tremayne, then at the tall, tense-looking man who had gone to stand a little closer to the singer. The man made no effort to return her smile.

"It's my fault, I'm afraid," Daniel said with great charm. As he spoke, Sunny sat calmly but alertly beside him, staring at the two strangers as if to emphasize the fact that her owner was her personal responsibility. "I'm probably one of your most faithful fans, Miss Tremayne, and I simply had to find out for myself if that incomparable voice was real or recorded."

He took a few steps and thrust his right hand forward as if he knew exactly where the others were standing. "As my wife said, I'm Daniel Kaine. And this is a real pleasure."

Jennifer watched him closely, suppressing the desire to roll her eyes. Her gaze then moved to the other man. She watched as his dark gray eyes darted from Daniel to Sunny, then back again to Daniel's face. Apparently he had just realized that Daniel was blind. His expression gradually relaxed, and the look of suspicion faded as he quickly stepped toward Dan, his hand extended.

At the same time, Vali Tremayne ran a slender hand through her hair—her incredible *mahogany* hair, Jennifer thought with admiration—and smiled uncertainly with what appeared to be a touch of shyness.

"I'm David Nathan Keye." The man's odd, whispering voice drew Jennifer's attention away from Vali. He was studying Dan's face with keen interest as they shook hands. "And I believe you already know that this is Vali Tremayne," he added, nodding his head in the singer's direction.

Jennifer had a fleeting impression of something slightly off balance in the man's face, then realized that his left eye had a faint droop, as if it were heavier than the right. She sensed a kind of melancholy about him, an odd contrast with what looked to be a glint of mischief in his eyes. He was attractive enough, she supposed. The light hair was a surprising accent to his dark skin, and his features were strong and pleasant. In spite of his appeal, however, Jennifer felt a certain ambiguity in the man that instinctively put her on guard.

His next words surprised her. "You're not by any chance a composer?" he asked Dan.

Hesitating for an instant, Dan answered, "I run a Christian radio station. But *you're* a composer," he quickly added. "And an impressive one. I know your music."

Keye looked surprised but continued to study Dan. "There's a Daniel Kaine who wrote an absolutely wonderful piece of music called *Daybreak,*" he said in his peculiar voice. "I believe he's . . . blind also. That's why I asked if you're a composer. I thought perhaps . . ."

Unable to contain herself any longer, Jennifer exclaimed with pride, "That's Daniel! He wrote *Daybreak!*"

Keye's facial expression brightened to a look of genuine admiration. Without hesitating, he gripped Daniel's hand again, this time shaking it more vigorously. "I've wanted to meet you since the first time I heard the score of *Daybreak,* just to tell you I think it's the most powerful piece of contemporary Christian music I've ever heard."

When Keye again turned his attention to Jennifer, she was surprised to see that there was a faint glow of warmth in his eyes. "And are you a musician, too, Mrs. Kaine?"

"Goodness, no! I'm—"

"A fantastic singer . . . and a terrific wife," Daniel finished for her.

"I'm *not*," Jennifer quickly protested. When Dan laughed, she glanced from him to Keye. "I mean, I hope I'm a good wife," she said, flustered, "but don't listen to anything else he says."

"Why don't we go inside and have some coffee?" the composer suggested. "Vali and I were just about to take a break when we noticed Trouble had disappeared again."

"Trouble?" Jennifer repeated blankly.

The singer spoke for the first time since their encounter, explaining softly, "My cat. Her name is Trouble."

"For good reason," Keye added sardonically. "Come on in," he offered, starting toward the porch.

"David, if they're on their honeymoon," Vali said uncertainly, "perhaps they'd rather not. . . ."

The composer looked from Vali to Jennifer. "Sorry," he said with an unexpectedly boyish grin. Reaching into the pocket of his striped shirt, he pulled out a stick of gum. The guarded cynicism so evident in his expression a few minutes before seemed to have totally vanished. He tucked the gum into his mouth, still smiling at Vali. When he looked at the small young woman standing next to him, a hint of an emotion that could only be tenderness filled his eyes. "I wasn't thinking."

"But we'd love to come in," Jennifer said quickly. "Wouldn't we, Daniel?"

Dan opened his mouth to say something but seemed to change his mind. With a knowing smile, he nodded. "Sure. Is this your home?" he asked Keye.

"I rent it." The composer took Vali's arm as they stepped back onto the porch and held the door for Dan and Jennifer.

"Do you mind my dog?" Dan asked him.

"Not at all," Keye assured him. "What's his name?"

"*Her* name," Daniel corrected. "Her name is Sunny." He

pursed his lips. "We'd better put our shoes on, Jennifer, before we go inside."

"Not necessary," Keye said with a smile. "My place is ever so humble. Just come as you are."

He waited for Sunny to guide Daniel through the doorway, then followed the others into a large, comfortably furnished living room dominated by a walnut grand piano and a bank of digital keyboards. The room was clean but cluttered. Stacks of music manuscripts were everywhere, and an empty coffee cup seemed to be on every table.

The composer crossed the room and took an indifferent swipe at the heap of manuscript paper and magazines on a table in front of the couch. "The place is messy but rat free," he said over his shoulder. "Let's go into the kitchen. It's probably cleaner, since I seldom use it. Say, you didn't see a slightly weird-looking cat anywhere, did you? Looks a bit like a confused, overweight rabbit with stubby ears?"

"I'm afraid not," Jennifer said, laughing at him.

"David keeps hoping she'll just vanish," Vali told them with a scolding glance at the composer. "The two of them have been at war since the first day they met."

"That was no meeting," Keye said archly. "That was a *blitzkrieg.*"

"She's only a kitten," Vali protested.

"With the heart of a cheetah," Keye returned, leading the way into a large, country kitchen with an adjoining glassed-in sunroom.

Watching the two of them, Jennifer wondered about the relationship between Vali Tremayne and David Nathan Keye. Like Daniel, she had recognized the composer's name right away. Not only had he written many of the recent hit songs on the Christian music charts, but he was a well-known keyboard artist as well. And he was obviously, her romantic spirit suggested, quite taken with the young singer standing at the kitchen counter pouring coffee. Remembering the tragic death of Vali's fiancé, Paul Alexander, and the numerous references to her inconsolable grief, Jennifer found herself hoping that Vali had indeed found someone else.

In a surprisingly brief time, the four of them fell into an easy, companionable conversation, sitting around the small oval table in the spacious kitchen, drinking coffee, and talking as casually as if they had known each other for years.

Jennifer could hear the respect in Dan's voice when he spoke to Keye. "You've got music all over the charts right now, David. You must write in your sleep."

The composer took a tray of cookies from Vali and brought it to the table, then straddled a chair. "Sometimes I wish I could. My music is actually my ministry, you see." He stopped, then added, "Obviously, this isn't the voice of a preacher. So I write music. Vali says I'm a workaholic." His smile was gentle as he watched the singer pull up a chair beside him.

"He doesn't know when to quit," Vali explained, glancing at Jennifer. "But if I could write music like David's, I probably wouldn't want to stop, either."

Jennifer stared at her, struck by Vali's flawless features. She remembered seeing pictures of her from years past. But she now realized the publicity photos hadn't even begun to reveal the singer's ethereal loveliness.

Her skin had a translucent quality, and her jade-colored eyes dominated her face with a haunting sadness that made it difficult to look away from her. Her hair—*that wonderful, incredible hair,* Jennifer thought—was an untamed cloud that formed a swirling, dramatic contrast to the delicate perfection of her face. Even dressed casually, in jeans and a striped rugby shirt, she looked like an exiled princess. Keye had even referred to her as "Princess" a couple of times during their conversation, and Jennifer had smiled at the appropriateness of the pet name.

Suddenly aware that she was staring, Jennifer turned her attention to Daniel, who was asking Vali Tremayne about her career. "Are you recording again, Miss Tremayne?"

The singer stared at him, her expression unmistakably troubled. "Please . . . call me Vali," she said quietly. "I . . . I don't know, about recording, I mean. It's been . . . a long time. David has been working with me on some arrangements, but I haven't . . . made any real decision yet."

She had a peculiar, static way of speaking that communicated a kind of uncertainty, a reluctance to assert herself. Combined with the faint hint of bewilderment in her eyes, she gave off an aura of skittishness, much like a young animal about to bolt.

"What Vali is much too polite to tell you," Keye quickly inserted, "is that her agent more or less strong-armed her into working with me. You see, a lot of people—myself foremost among them—want to see Vali back in the industry. My producer and I are trying to sell her on the idea of using my music as her return vehicle."

Vali went on staring at the table as Keye spoke.

"Well, that sounds like a great idea to me," Daniel said lightly, as if he could sense the tension in the room.

Keye continued to study Vali intently as Dan went on. "You've been doing keyboards for a number of artists, haven't you? In addition to your own composing?"

"Actually, that's what gave me my start when I moved from the West Coast," Keye replied, finally dragging his gaze away from Vali. "Some people in Nashville knew my work and got me a few jobs. Eventually I was able to get a couple of my own numbers recorded."

"You're from California, then?" Daniel asked.

"For the most part." The composer flashed a brief smile, then let the conversation drop for a moment as he poured himself another cup of coffee. "Until October, at least, I'm a Buckeye. My rent is paid until then."

"Jennifer's a Buckeye," Dan said, smiling in her direction. "A transplanted one, that is. She's learning to become a Mountaineer now."

"A Mountaineer? That's West Virginia, isn't it?" the composer asked.

"Shepherd Valley," Dan replied with a nod. "Just a little town at the foot of some great mountains."

"And you own a Christian radio station? That means you're one of the fellows who can help make or break my career."

Dan laughed easily. "I'm afraid we don't have that kind of influence. But you don't have anything to worry about—you're well on your way."

"That may depend on whether or not I can get Vali to sing my music," Keye said, turning to look at the singer.

His remark disturbed Jennifer; it sounded as if the composer intended to use Vali. She knew it was none of her business, but something about the quiet young singer inspired her protective instincts.

Unexpectedly, Vali smiled at him. "David, you make it sound as if I had to be forced to work with you."

Keye shrugged, but the smile he gave her was gentle. "My rent's only paid until October, Princess. I'm running out of time to come up with that one special number you simply can't resist."

"Well, you'll certainly be doing all of us a big favor," Daniel said to Keye, "if you can get her back into a recording studio."

The composer nodded. "There's a host of people out there who agree with you, Daniel." His gaze darted to the kitchen window. "However," he said, "you're about to meet someone who *doesn't.*"

His whispered comment was sharply punctuated by a loud, demanding knock on the side door. Sunny roused from her place by Dan's chair with a warning growl, then stood waiting alertly at his side. Dan reached to gentle her with his hand and a soft word of reassurance.

Before the last thud died away, a big, dark-haired man pushed through the door, charging into the kitchen as if he needed no invitation. He stood staring at the four of them through narrowed eyes, his expression questioning and seemingly hostile.

Without getting up, David gave the man a thin smile. "Won't you come in, Graham?"

Jennifer couldn't take her eyes off the other man. His handsome features seemed vaguely familiar. Not quite as tall as Daniel, he looked to be about twenty pounds heavier. She would guess him to be in his early to mid-thirties. His well-tailored gray suit looked decidedly out of place in these casual lakefront surroundings. The impression was that of a somewhat arrogant, imperious personality.

He flicked a sharp glance at David, then frowned at Vali. "You might let me know when you're going to be away from your cottage for such a long time, Vali. I've been trying to call you for well over two hours now." His voice was refined, clipped, almost British in nuance.

Jennifer flinched in surprise when Vali stood, pushing her chair back so abruptly it almost toppled.

"Oh, Graham—I'm so sorry! David and I were working on some new numbers . . . and then we met Daniel and Jennifer—" She stopped, glanced for an instant at Jennifer, then turned back to the man now towering over her. "I suppose I didn't think. . . ."

The man called "Graham" cast a withering look at Keye, then raked both Jennifer and Daniel with a look of impatience before returning his attention to Vali. "That's becoming somewhat of a habit with you these days, isn't it, dear?" he asked icily. "Not thinking."

Vali colored and began wringing her hands. "I . . . should have called you. I forgot."

"I would think by now you'd know how I worry about you, Vali."

"Yes . . . I do know, Graham. . . ." Vali's voice had softened until it was almost as much of a whisper as Keye's.

The composer now stood, his eyes glinting with an unpleasant look of challenge. "It was my fault, Graham—as usual," he rasped. "When I'm working with Vali, I'm afraid I have a tendency to forget everything else but . . . the music."

In the face of the other's cold silence, Keye continued. "Let me introduce you to Daniel and Jennifer Kaine. Fellow musicians— and new friends. Daniel, Jennifer—this is Graham Alexander. A very . . . close friend of Vali's."

THREE

J ENNIFER almost choked. *Graham Alexander.* The twin brother of Vali's deceased fiancé. There had been a lot of publicity at the time of Paul Alexander's death, including a number of references to his brother, a research scientist, and his mother, an internationally known novelist. Staring hard at the big man with the chilling eyes, Jennifer was surprised she hadn't seen the resemblance immediately. The man standing across the table from her looked enough like his dead brother to be mistaken for him, except for the extra pounds he was carrying. Or was it the lack of Paul Alexander's trademark smile that made the difference?

Graham Alexander offered only a grudging nod in acknowledgment of the introduction before turning to Vali. "You *did* remember that we're meeting Mother at the Twine House for dinner?"

"Of course, Graham," she replied. "I wouldn't forget something like that. I'm looking forward to it."

Graham Alexander's gaze swept over Vali, and Jennifer felt a pang of sympathy for the lovely young singer, who was clearly ill at ease. "You'll be changing into something more suitable, I imagine?" Alexander said, an edge still in his voice.

Vali looked at him blankly, then glanced down at her jeans. "Oh . . . yes. This isn't . . . I was planning to change."

David crossed his arms over his chest and stared at Graham

17

Alexander. "I didn't realize the Twine House is formal," he said, lifting a hand to his face in a mock gesture of dismay. "And to think I went there in *my* jeans last night. It's a wonder they didn't toss me out."

The scientist settled a look of contempt on Keye, his silent glare making a statement of its own.

David shrugged, "Ah, well . . . what would you expect from a beach-bum musician. Right, Graham?"

If his intention was to annoy Alexander, it seemed to work. He scowled, adjusted the knot of his silk tie, and turned to Vali. "I'll pick you up at six. We're to meet Mother at six-fifteen." Without waiting for an answer, he pecked her lightly on the cheek, turned one more scathing look at David Nathan Keye, then turned and walked out the door, slamming it behind him.

It was quiet in the kitchen for a long, awkward moment after he left. Vali was obviously embarrassed, and Jennifer could sense the tension in David as well.

Daniel finally broke the silence. "We should be going, Jennifer," he said, standing and reaching for her hand. "We haven't even unpacked all our things yet."

Keye and Vali followed them outside, where they stood talking for a few more moments. Dan started to shake hands with the composer, then stopped suddenly. "I wonder . . . would the two of you mind if I looked at you? With my hands?" He smiled ingenuously. "To tell you the truth, it's a little more than a blind man's curiosity. I thought it would be something to tell my kids someday."

Jennifer was surprised when Vali stepped up to him without hesitating. "Your children probably won't know who you're talking about, Daniel," she said softly, "but go right ahead."

As Dan explored the lovely face at his fingertips, Jennifer smiled, remembering his gentleness the first time he had "looked" at her.

After he dropped his hands back to his side, Daniel turned toward David. "I'll just bet you're not that pretty."

The composer's eyes narrowed for an instant as he studied Dan. Jennifer thought she sensed a fleeting look of anxiety in his expression, but he covered it with a brief smile. "A keenly accurate assumption, Daniel." His whispery laugh sounded forced and nervous, but he bore Dan's examination of his face with seeming good humor.

Jennifer was puzzled by her husband's questioning frown as he finally let his hands drop away from Keye's face. "It's always interesting to me when I finally put a face with a voice," Dan said casually. "You surprised me, David. I pictured you without a beard—and a little heavier."

Keye lifted one eyebrow skeptically. "What? Not Quasimodo?" Dan frowned in earnest.

The composer laughed. "The voice. People react to it in different ways."

"What caused it?" Dan asked him directly.

Keye shrugged. "Accident. My vocal chords were crushed." He paused, then added, "I read about what happened to you in some of the news releases for *Daybreak.* A drunk driver, wasn't it?"

Dan nodded slowly, and Jennifer knew he was about to ask Keye something else. Instead, he stooped to pat Sunny on the head, then straightened and shook hands with Keye. After a few more good-byes, they parted. Both Vali and David stood in the doorway, waving as Jennifer and Dan started down the walk and turned toward their own cottage.

Later that night, Jennifer and Daniel walked hand in hand along the shore, allowing Sunny to run free. The air was still warm, holding no hint of the approaching autumn that usually came

19

early to northern Ohio. It was the kind of night made for hushed voices, soft music, and quiet laughter.

"What do you think of our new acquaintances?" Daniel asked as they walked along.

Jennifer didn't answer right away. "I'm not sure," she finally said. "They're . . . a little different. Nice," she added, "but different."

"How old would you guess David to be?" Dan said.

Jennifer thought for a moment. "Early thirties, at least. He has a good bit of gray in his hair, but it's mixed in with blond, so you don't really notice it at first." She paused. "What did you think of him?"

Daniel shrugged. "I'm not sure. For some reason, I found him difficult to visualize." After a moment he added, "There's something . . . peculiar about his skin."

Jennifer looked at him. "Peculiar? What do you mean?"

"It's . . . too supple for a man his age." Dan gave a short laugh. "I know it sounds odd, but he has the skin of a teenager. And around his hairline . . ." He didn't finish.

"His hairline?"

Again Dan laughed and shook his head. "I must be losing my touch."

Jennifer groaned. "If that was a pun, you've done better, Daniel."

He grinned. "Humor me." He said nothing else for a moment. "You're sure he's in his thirties?" he finally asked, still sounding puzzled.

"Definitely."

"Hm. His left eye droops a little, doesn't it?"

Jennifer glanced up at him. "You don't miss much, do you? Yes, as a matter of fact, his eye *does* droop. Just a little, enough to make him look rather . . . cunning."

"Cunning? That's a detective-story word, Jennifer. What do you mean?"

She considered. "Smart. A little devious, I think. But nice." She hesitated. "That's the strange thing about him—overall, he seems to be very nice, good-natured, charming. Definitely intelligent. But there's something else that doesn't quite fit, and I'm not sure what it is. He's—"

"Tense," Dan finished. "Explosive. Like a volcano about to erupt."

"What?" Jennifer was only half listening. "Let's stop here a minute, Daniel. I've got a stone or something in my sandal."

"I'd say he's under a great deal of stress," Dan mused.

"Mmm. He limps . . . did I tell you?" She pulled a small stone from the toe of her sandal. "Like his leg is stiff."

Sunny came bounding up to them, and Dan stooped to rub her ears, then straightened. "And the lovely Vali is like . . . a frightened fawn," he remarked.

Jennifer drew in a sharp breath. "That's *exactly* what she makes me think of! I couldn't have been any more surprised by her, Daniel. You hear her sing, and you get this fantastic sense of power and control. But in person, she's actually . . . *shy*, I think. Even insecure."

They started walking again. "What about Graham Alexander?" Jennifer said, linking her arm with Dan's. "Do you suppose they're engaged? I didn't see a ring."

"He certainly seems to have some sort of hold on her, doesn't he?"

"I thought he was insufferable. What kind of vibes did *you* get about him?"

He grimaced. "I don't get *vibes*, Jennifer. I'm blind, not psychic."

"Ooh, touchy." She grinned at him, savoring the way the soft puffs of wind off the lake lifted strands of his hair, ruffling it and tossing it gently over his forehead. "But what did you think of him?"

His tone was puzzled when he answered. "I'm not sure. They're an interesting trio, aren't they?"

"Well, I can tell you one thing," Jennifer said decisively. "David is in love with Vali."

Dan came to an abrupt halt, and a ghost of a smile flickered across his face. "And Daniel," he said softly as he gathered her into his arms, "is in love with Jennifer." Without warning, he lowered his head to kiss her lightly. Then again, this time not so lightly.

"Daniel . . ." Jennifer's protest was halfhearted as she returned his kiss. "There are people on the beach."

"Then what we need to do," he murmured against her hair, "is get off the beach."

FOUR

THE man was almost asleep when the demanding shrill of the bedside phone shattered the silence. He bolted upright in the darkness and reached for the receiver.

"Who are they?"

Groggy, he was slow to react to the impatient voice on the other end of the line. "They?"

"The blind man and the woman—who are they?"

He looked at the digital clock on the nightstand. Twenty minutes after midnight. "Kaine. Daniel and Jennifer Kaine. There's no problem with them—they'll be gone in a few days."

"Anyone new could be a problem at this time."

"I hardly think we need to feel threatened by a blind man and his wife." The man's voice dripped sarcasm.

There was silence for a moment. "Only the singer is a threat. And, as you've so confidently assured us, the solution to that particular problem is forthcoming." The caller's voice grew even more harsh. "May I ask again . . . *when?*"

The man sighed, trying for patience. "Soon. I need a few more weeks, I told you."

"No. One week, no more. You've already wasted far too much time."

"Everything is working out exactly as I planned. She remembers nothing, and I've become very important to her. The rest is a matter of time."

"No, my friend. Either you have a definite solution, a commitment, within the next week, or we eliminate her." The caller hesitated, then added, "Which is what we should have done in the first place."

"That is, and always has been, an extremely foolish idea!" the man snapped. "She's far too well known, and it would simply be too much of a coincidence after the airplane crash. No," he said firmly, "my way is better. You'll see."

"Well . . . we shall hope that you are right. In the meantime, we'll be helping you however we can."

"What do you mean?"

"Simply that the more disoriented and confused she grows, the more dependent upon you she will become."

"I can handle this alone," the man said sharply.

"Of course you can. But we're in this together, are we not? The least I can do is to lend you a bit of assistance."

"I'm warning you," he grated, "if you do something to spoil what I've accomplished so far—"

"Do not warn me of *anything,* my friend." The voice was soft, the threat implicit, the click of the phone final.

Only after he replaced the receiver did the man finally switch on the lamp. He sat on the side of the bed for a few more minutes, then stood. With a scowling glance at the telephone, he threw on a bathrobe. One week. Not nearly long enough.

But he knew there would be no more time, no more delays. Somehow, he would have to move everything up.

FIVE

I REALLY respect your courage, darlin'," Dan said with a wondering shake of his head. "But doesn't the idea of me in an amusement park remind you of Daniel in the lions' den?"

Jennifer poured him a second cup of coffee and refilled her own cup before sitting down at the table beside him. "As I recall," she said pointedly, *"that* Daniel got out without a scratch."

"Besides, amusement parks close after Labor Day," he said mildly, reaching for his third doughnut.

"But Cedar Point is open for two weekends *after* Labor Day. And this happens to be the last weekend. Come on, Daniel, I really want to go. It'll be fun."

"Fun for who?"

"Fun for *whom*. Will you go?"

"Absolutely not."

She sighed. "I've wanted to go back to Cedar Point for years." Her voice was soft, intentionally plaintive. "It would make this week even more special."

"Ah . . . sentimentality. Nice touch, Jennifer. But I'm still not going."

She poked him.

"Jennifer, you wouldn't want me to think that the success of our honeymoon depends on me making a fool of myself at an amusement park, would you?" He took a bite of the chocolate-covered doughnut.

"Since when are you intimidated by a new adventure?" she challenged. "Daniel, I can still remember how amazed I was—and impressed—when I first started working with you and discovered how different you were from what I had expected."

He finished his doughnut, wiped the chocolate from his mouth, and leaned back in his chair. Crossing his arms comfortably over his chest, he smiled—a wide, knowing smile that plainly said he knew what was coming but wanted to hear it anyway.

"Why, I distinctly remember, Daniel, being totally dumbfounded at the way you handled things. I mean, I'd always had the idea that people with disabilities are somewhat . . . insecure."

He nodded wisely.

"But you were so extroverted and authoritative, so confident and willing to try new things—you shattered every preconceived notion I'd ever had."

He made a brief, self-deprecating gesture with his hand. "Aw shucks, honey."

"In fact," she went on, ignoring him, *"you* made *me* feel inhibited sometimes; you were so willing to take a chance, eager to try new experiences. . . ."

Laughing, he put up a restraining hand. "This is good, darlin'— not one of your better routines, but still good."

She studied his face hopefully. "Are you thinking about it, Daniel?"

"Mm. Maybe."

When he began to drum his fingers on the table, Jennifer was pretty sure she'd won.

"Does this place have a roller coaster?" he suddenly asked, stopping his rhythmic tapping.

"Does it have—Daniel, Cedar Point probably has more roller coasters than any other amusement park in the country," she announced smugly, then paused. "But you wouldn't want to ride a roller coaster, would you? I mean, wouldn't that be kind of scary when you can't see anything?"

He grinned wickedly. "It's what you *can* see that terrifies you on a roller coaster. OK," he said decisively. "We'll go. *And*—we will ride all the roller coasters in the park. Together." He crossed his arms over his chest again, his smile daring her to refuse.

"I . . . ah . . . actually, I've never been on a roller coaster, Daniel."

His grin became a full-scale smirk. "Jennifer," he drawled, sitting forward on his chair and rubbing his hands together with obvious glee, "this is going to be an unforgettable day."

The day couldn't have been more perfect for their plans. The temperature was in the low seventies, the air was dry, and the sky looked like frosted blue glass.

"It's going to be *extremely* crowded," Jennifer remarked as she craned her neck to study the long lines waiting at the entry gates. "There must be dozens of people ahead of us."

"Just don't lose me in the crowd," Dan said.

Hearing what sounded like a touch of anxiety in his voice, Jennifer glanced up at him. "Does it bother you a lot, being without Sunny? I didn't think we'd be able to go on the rides if she came with us."

"I don't especially like crowds, even with Sunny," he admitted. "It's too easy to get confused."

Jennifer frowned, annoyed at her thoughtlessness. "Oh, Daniel, I'm sorry! I was so intent on having my own way I didn't even stop to think how difficult this might be for you. Listen, we don't have to go in—we'll leave right now."

He covered her hand on his forearm with his own. "No way, darlin'. If you think I'm going to miss a chance to ride all those roller coasters, think again."

She thought his smile might be a little forced. "Daniel, are you *sure?*"

"Absolutely. I can't wait to—"

Jennifer and Dan both whirled around in surprise when they heard a rasping voice call their names. Standing off to one side was Vali Tremayne, accompanied by David Nathan Keye, who smiled and waved what looked like a handful of passes.

"I can get all of us in on these," he said. "Let me treat, OK?"

Without waiting for a reply, he and Vali walked over. Keye touched Dan lightly on the shoulder in a friendly gesture, then linked arms with both Jennifer and Vali as he began to move around the line and up to the entry gate. Jennifer held Dan's hand tightly so they wouldn't get separated.

Once through the gate, after thanking Keye for their free admission, Jennifer turned to Vali and said, "So you decided to take advantage of this last weekend, too?"

"I twisted her arm," David said with a grin. "I love amusement parks. And I figured if this one is so great that I heard about it in California, it must really be something."

"You won't be disappointed, David," Jennifer told him, glancing around. "Oh, look—here comes the clown band!"

A parade of wildly dressed, zany clowns came strutting down a nearby lane, playing a variety of instruments and shouting among themselves.

After they passed, David took Vali by the hand and looked thoughtfully from Dan to Jennifer. "Say, you two wouldn't want to pair up with us for the day, would you?"

"David," Vali quickly objected, "they're on their honeymoon, remember?"

"Oh—right. Sorry; of course you'd rather be alone—"

Jennifer elbowed Dan, who flinched, then responded to his cue. "No, that sounds good to us. Jennifer?"

She nodded her head eagerly. "We'd love to!"

Vali searched Jennifer's eyes. "Are you sure? We'd understand if you'd rather not."

"No, really—it'll be fun."

"Well, then, what are we waiting for?" David studied Dan for a moment, then asked matter-of-factly, "What's easiest for you, Dan? Walking on the outside or in between?"

Daniel replied without hesitating. "The outside, with Jennifer guiding me. She's not as good as Sunny," he added dryly, "but I guess I can't be particular today." Jennifer dug him lightly in the ribs, and they started off.

Over the next two hours, they rode the train, ate french fries; rode the log ride, ate hot dogs; rode the Tilt-A-Whirl, ate cotton candy; rode the bumper cars, and ate pizza.

"I'm going to be sick," David groaned, rubbing at a dab of tomato sauce on the front of his striped shirt.

"You deserve to be," Vali told him.

Jennifer didn't miss Vali's faint blush—of pleasure, she thought— when David hugged her to his side and said, "Have a little pity, Princess. I'm turning green."

"What we need," Daniel announced, "is a change of pace. A nice leisurely ride that won't stir up or dislocate anything."

"Wise counsel, Daniel." The composer adjusted his sunglasses with one finger.

They started walking again. "We'll have to bring Jason up here next year," Dan said.

"He'd love it," Jennifer agreed.

"Jason?" Vali gave them a questioning look.

"Our son."

David threw them a somewhat startled glance.

"We have an adopted son," Jennifer explained. "Well, almost adopted. It won't be final for a few months yet. Dan was planning to adopt Jason before we got married, so now we're finalizing it in both our names."

"How old is he?" asked Vali.

"Almost nine," Jennifer answered. "And he's absolutely adorable." Jason was staying with Dan's parents for the duration of the honeymoon, and already Jennifer found herself missing the small towhead who had so quickly charmed his way into her heart.

"Well, Daniel, what nice, leisurely ride do you recommend for us?" David asked as they started walking again.

Dan considered. "The Ferris wheel, I think."

"Oh, no!" Jennifer said, a little too quickly.

"Oh, no?" repeated her husband.

"It's too . . . high."

"Are you afraid of heights, Jennifer?" Vali looked genuinely concerned.

"She won't admit it, but she is," Dan told them.

"I wouldn't say I'm *afraid,* exactly."

Dan gave her a smug look. "I thought you believed in confronting your fears."

"There's no fear to confront here, Daniel," she countered. "I simply don't want to get on an airborne Tinkertoy with my stomach feeling like a cement mixer. Not all of us," she said pointedly, "have steel tubing for a digestive tract."

His grin broadened. "From what you've told me, it'll come in real handy when I have to start eating your cooking."

Jennifer muttered under her breath, then said reluctantly, "Oh, all right. We'll ride the Ferris wheel. But don't say I didn't warn you."

Vali stood waiting in line, vaguely wishing Jennifer hadn't agreed to "confront her fears." Actually, she didn't much like this ride either. But she found herself more likely to keep quiet about her own fears—surely far more numerous than Jennifer Kaine's—when she was with David. For some inexplicable reason, she didn't want him seeing what Graham called her *neuroses*. David obviously thought well of her. Lately she'd been surprised by how much she wanted to keep his respect.

They had become good friends in these past few weeks of working together. At least, *she* counted *him* as a friend. For David's part, he made her a little uncomfortable sometimes by hinting—strongly—that he was attracted to her as a woman, not only as a friend. He was recklessly candid about it, too—even around Graham. In fact, he sometimes seemed intent on deliberately *goading* Graham.

Last night, after learning that Graham would be in Cleveland for two days, David had become disconcertingly blunt about his feelings.

"You're not engaged to the man, right?" he had asked Vali directly.

"Not exactly, but—"

"I don't see a ring, Vali."

"He's asked me to marry him."

"And have you given him an answer?"

"Well, I have to be . . . sure."

"And you're not?"

"I—almost . . ."

"Almost doesn't count, Princess."

"David—"

They had been sitting beside each other on the piano bench, and he had flashed that impish grin of his and cuffed her lightly on the chin with a gentle fist. But suddenly his dark gray eyes had lost their glint of mischief, darkening to an expression that made Vali's heart lurch and threaten to betray her loyalty to Graham. He had taken her gently by the shoulders and held her captive with his searching look. "Vali, surely you know that you've become very important to me. Give me a chance, Princess . . . that's all I'm asking . . . just a chance."

Without understanding why, Vali had become almost angry with him. She resented the ease with which he threatened her orderly lifestyle. She had pushed him away. "I won't work with you if you're going to act like this!"

He had apologized at once—but only for upsetting her. Not for being interested in her. And he still looked at her . . . that way . . . the way that said he cared about her. Deeply.

David unnerved her, exasperated her, at times almost frightened her with his intensity. And yet she trusted him. Why was that, she wondered? How could she trust such a troublesome, stubborn, impudent man? A man so different from Graham. Graham was so strong, so dependable, so . . . in control.

"Penny for them, Princess," David whispered at her side.

Vali jumped, then locked gazes with him, caught off guard, as always, by the affection in his eyes.

With a small laugh, she told him, "I'm afraid I was wishing Jennifer weren't so brave . . . about facing her fears."

His expression quickly sobered. "We don't have to go on this thing if you'd rather not."

"No—I'm just . . . a little jittery, I suppose." Vali brightened and smiled at him. "We came to do it all, remember?"

He slipped one long arm around her shoulders to move her through the gate. "Here we go, then."

Vali stepped into the gondola, uncomfortably aware that the operator was staring curiously at her. After getting into the seat, she glanced up at the man's face, unsettled by what appeared to be a glint of amusement in his darkly shadowed eyes. Quickly she looked away.

Dan and Jennifer were in the car just above them, and Vali could hear them laughing as the car began to move. *What a special pair they are,* she thought with a smile. That wonderful, incredible blind man somehow gave others a sense of security in his presence—and so did his lovely Jennifer, with her laughing dark eyes, ready wit, and totally unselfish interest in others.

"I love to see you smile like that," David said. He still had his arm around Vali, and he gently squeezed her shoulder. "But I'm almost jealous because I don't know why you're smiling."

"The Kaines," she said simply, looking out over the park. "I was thinking about how special they are."

"Ah, there goes my ego again. I was hoping you were thinking of me."

"David, you're impossible," Vali scolded, captured by the smile in his eyes when she turned to look at him.

Disturbed by her own feelings, she quickly looked away to scan the crowd below. As they began to ascend, she caught sight of what she thought was a familiar face.

A man, completely bald, stood motionless in the throng of people at the base of the ride. Vali was certain he was staring up at her. Not tall, but square and somewhat heavy, he had the thick, overmuscled appearance of a boxer past his prime. In a conservative dark suit, he looked grossly out of place in his surroundings.

The sight of him unnerved her, for she felt a slight sense of recognition as she looked at him. Yet she was positive she had never seen him before. David said something to her just then, and by the time she glanced back into the crowd, the man had disappeared.

Vali was still trying to identify the stranger in her memory as they climbed to the top. Suddenly a loud *crunch* threw her against the safety bar, and the ride came to an abrupt stop.

SIX

VALI heard Jennifer cry out above. At the same time, the nervous laughter and uneasy mutterings of the other riders increased around them.

David had pulled her back away from the safety bar when the car lurched, but Vali desperately wished they weren't so near the top of the ride. There was just enough breeze to make the car rock gently back and forth, and she swallowed hard a couple of times against the sick wrenching of her stomach.

David tightened his protective hold on her and gently coaxed her face against his shoulder. "OK?" he whispered.

Vali nodded, grateful for his warm closeness. "Is something wrong, do you think?"

"I'm not sure."

She glanced up, and his troubled expression unsettled her even more. She tried to laugh. "Well, whatever it is, I wish it could have gone wrong when we were a little closer to the ground."

He squeezed her shoulder. "It's all right. Probably just a new operator learning his job at our expense." With his free hand, he tugged lightly on a wave of Vali's hair. "Actually, I paid him to keep us up here for a bit. Got you at my mercy now, pretty lady."

Vali kept her face burrowed against his shoulder, unwilling to move for fear of making the car sway even more. "Don't make fun, David. I don't like this."

He rested his chin lightly on the top of her head. "We're all right, Princess," he whispered hoarsely into her hair. "Don't you know by now I wouldn't let anything hurt you?"

Vali looked up at him, feeling her heart turn over when she saw the way he was caressing her with his gaze.

They remained that way for a long moment before a shutter seemed to close in his eyes, and he looked away. He continued to hold her, but now there was nothing more than an awkward silence between them.

Fifteen minutes passed; the voices of riders in the other cars gradually grew more agitated. When David tapped her lightly on the shoulder and pointed to the ground, Vali looked, then sighed with relief. The ride operator was helping two young girls out of the car closest to the ground. Then he began to lower the wheel so that each car could empty its passengers. Slowly and methodically every gondola was lowered and emptied until it was David and Vali's turn.

Without knowing why, Vali jerked her hand away when the operator reached out to help her. Saying nothing, the young man raked a thin wisp of blond hair away from his forehead, staring hard at her as David got out.

"Was there a problem?" he asked the operator.

At the sound of David's whisper-voice, the man shot him a questioning look. "No big deal," he muttered. "Slight problem on the axle. Sorry for the delay."

Vali saw David give the man a long, studying look before leading her to the gate, where Dan and Jennifer stood waiting.

"So much for your idea of a nice, leisurely ride, Daniel!" Jennifer was teasing him as Vali and David approached.

Dan wore a sheepish grin. "You have to admit, it gave you a good chance to confront your fears."

"That was *not* a confrontation, Daniel," asserted his wife. "That was an *assault.*"

"I think we owe Jennifer the ride of her choice about now," David offered, and everyone quickly agreed.

Somehow the ride of Jennifer's choice got postponed. As the four of them walked by the *Magnum* roller coaster, David mumbled something to Daniel, and the two stopped near the crowd waiting to get on.

"It's a conspiracy." Jennifer turned to Vali. "Are you going on?"

Vali looked at her, then at David, who grinned and gave her a thumbs-up sign.

"Yes," the singer replied, much to Jennifer's surprise and dismay. "I think I will."

Jennifer swallowed. "Then so will I."

Dan looked suspiciously gratified.

Once they arrived at the end of the line, however, Jennifer's resolve began to flag.

"Oh dear . . ." She attempted a weak laugh. "I am *so* disappointed . . . but it looks as though I won't be able to do this after all."

"Why not?" Dan asked her skeptically.

"Well, you see, there's a sign here that says you have to be *this* tall in order to go on the ride, and I'm afraid I don't measure up. I'll just go sit down on a bench and wait."

Dan held her hand with an iron grip. "Nice try, Jennifer. Now, come on."

Jennifer eyed the wicked-looking coaster one more time, swallowed hard, then moved, with all the enthusiasm of a condemned prisoner en route to the execution chamber, to take her place in line. Somewhere behind them, she heard someone mention, in an awestruck voice, the fact that you could see the "first hill" from anywhere in the park.

Feeling a little sick, she stopped to tie her tennis shoe. As she straightened, a rather odd-looking man just off to her right caught her attention. Unnerved by his pale-eyed stare, she suddenly realized that it was Vali who was the focus of his attention, not herself.

She watched him closely. His dark suit and tie were peculiarly out of place in the amusement park, especially on such a warm day. Involuntarily, Jennifer shuddered. Something about the man seemed strangely sinister. She glanced away for just a second, then looked again, disturbed to find his eyes now riveted on her. Jennifer turned her back on him, but it seemed that she could still feel his malevolent stare burning into her. *Probably just some oddball voyeur,* she thought with distaste.

"What's it look like, Jennifer?" Daniel asked, suddenly breaking into her unsettled thoughts.

Jennifer stared up at the coaster, then froze. The twisting, convoluted tracks just ahead rose to an inconceivable height—a *deadly* height! She swallowed down a soft sob of denial.

"Jennifer? What does it look like?"

She looked from the *Magnum* to her husband. "Like my worst nightmare," she said thickly. "Daniel . . . you don't want to do this. Trust me."

He rubbed his hands together gleefully. "My kind of coaster."

"Be quiet, Daniel. I'm praying."

"Jennifer—"

"I'm *serious,* Daniel. I *am* praying."

"Boy-oh-boy." He grinned with pleasure. "This is going to be good!"

When the car started up the first incline, Jennifer decided with guarded relief that maybe it wouldn't be so bad after all. She didn't care for the clanking and grinding and lurching, and the hill seemed to go on forever. Still, the safety bar seemed secure, and Daniel's large, solid frame next to her gave her what she hoped wasn't a false sense of protection.

It was the first drop that jolted her with the blood-freezing reality of just how wrong she had been. It was a terrible feeling, a stomach-crushing, mind-exploding feeling.

"*Daniel!*" she screamed. "We're going to fall out!"

"People don't fall out of roller coasters, Jennifer!" he shouted back. "It's got something to do with centrifugal force!"

Centrifugal force! Was that all that was holding them in place? "I *hate* this, Daniel!"

"No, you don't!" he yelled with assurance above the din of screaming people and banging clatter. "You're having fun, Jennifer!"

Jennifer somehow managed to open her eyes long enough to turn and look at her husband. With disbelief she saw his upraised arms, the look of pure pleasure on his face, and for heaven's sake, the crazy man was *laughing out loud!*

"It doesn't go any faster, does it, Daniel?" she screamed in terror, unable to hear her own voice as they hugged a death-defying loop.

"Right, honey! It'll go a *lot* faster! You'll love it!" He waved his arms a little more. "Man, this is a *good* one!"

The wind slapped Jennifer's face. The noise shattered her eardrums. The creaking, clanging metal tracks rose and fell. People screamed. Daniel laughed. Jennifer whimpered.

"Are your hands up, Jennifer?"

"My entire body is paralyzed, Daniel Kaine! The only thing up is my blood pressure!"

"I told you you'd love it, didn't I?"

"Daniel, don't you *hear* me?!"

Then she knew. They were going to plummet off the track. The whole chain of cars was simply going to topple off and go flying into the crowd. She felt the car lean, felt herself being lifted from the seat, then pushed back into place. She looked down, over the side, into the trees. She saw the lake . . . and screamed. Terrorized, she twisted and threw her arms around Daniel's middle, pushing her head under his upraised arm. Again she screamed, this time into the hard, safe warmth of his ribs.

As she stepped out of the car, her entire body shaking, Jennifer silently promised herself that she would never—absolutely *never*—let him talk her into anything ever again.

The carousel was their final stop before leaving the park, each of them declaring that Jennifer, good sport that she'd been, deserved at least one quiet, *safe* ride.

It was a beautiful carousel with ornate cornices, vivid panels, elegant chariots, and a choice of gallopers, jumpers, and flying horses. The calliope music was loud and happy.

Jennifer and Vali chose two proud-looking jumpers, with the men opting for flying horses on the outside.

"Now this is more like it," Jennifer declared as Dan gave her a hand up to her mount before getting on his own somewhat wild-looking stallion. "I love these things," she told him. "When I was a little girl, I used to ride them over and over again, pretending I was an Indian princess or a lady in King Arthur's court."

Dan grinned as he settled onto his horse. Directly in front of them, Vali and David talked in hushed, serious tones, making Jennifer smile at their obvious attraction for each other.

She couldn't help but wonder who would be best for Vali—David Keye or Graham Alexander. Not that it was any of her business, she reminded herself, but she wasn't sure that she actually approved of either man.

Perhaps she was being unfair to Graham Alexander. The scientist obviously cared about the lovely young singer. And while David's interest might be just as genuine, it might *not* be as good for Vali. Certainly he was a more disturbing kind of man than Alexander appeared to be. Clever and witty and outrageously unconventional one moment, he could turn suddenly quiet and withdrawn the next.

Ah, well, she thought with a tender glance at her husband sitting quietly next to her, *not every man can be a Daniel.*

She looked around the platform, taking in the horses and the people astride them. At the operator's stand, a small, red-haired young man with glasses was talking with a dark, lanky youth. She saw the redhead move to start the ride, then stop at something the other boy said. He looked at his wristwatch, then jumped from the platform, leaving his companion to operate the carousel.

Impatient, Jennifer turned to look at the crowd of bystanders. She drew in a sharp breath of surprise when she caught a glimpse of a familiar face. Standing well behind a line of observers was the same man she had seen earlier at the *Magnum,* the bald man in the dark business suit.

Jennifer's gaze locked with the man's pale, hard stare. He narrowed his eyes, then glanced from her to Vali before backing out of the crowd and walking off. The ride began to move. Jennifer tried to keep track of him as they circled, but he disappeared.

Perhaps her uneasiness was foolish, but this second appearance of the peculiar-acting stranger troubled her. She was sure she had never seen him before, yet something about him made her feel threatened. More specifically, she realized, he made her feel frightened for Vali.

Abruptly, Jennifer tried to shake off her feelings, determined that nothing was going to spoil this ride. She glanced over at Dan, relishing the sight of his strong, bronzed profile as he sat smiling on the flying horse.

The sun was just beginning to fade below the horizon. It had been a magical day. Jennifer smiled fondly at the memory of the young girl who had once ridden this same carousel, her head filled with wonderful, romantic dreams. Now she had her very own prince, and he was stronger and more handsome than any of the leading men of her schoolgirl dreams. She was in love, she was happy, and life was good.

Caught up in her temporary euphoria, the gradual change in the calliope's volume and the slight shift in rotation of the platform escaped her notice until Dan called out to her. "Jennifer?" His voice was sharp with concern. "What's going on?"

At the same time, Jennifer saw Vali dart a worried look at David, who in turn cast a measuring look at the carousel's machinery.

The speed was still increasing, the music growing continually louder. Jennifer heard children begin to cry and saw several people move in closer as they watched. She could hear a growing buzz of alarm among the crowd, and she felt her heart lurch, then race even faster than the music.

Like a macabre dream, the platform whirled faster and faster, horses flying, chariots thumping, the grinding calliope now loud and ugly and distorted.

Jennifer cried out to Dan, who slid off his mount and moved in beside her to wrap a steadying arm around her waist. David jumped from his horse and went to Vali.

With his free hand, Daniel covered Jennifer's white-knuckled grip on the carousel rod. "Can you see anything?" he asked her. "The ride operator? Where is he?"

They were flying now, faces outside the fence whirling by in a dizzying kaleidoscope.

"I can't see anything!" Jennifer cried hoarsely. "Daniel, don't let go of me!"

In answer, he tightened his grip protectively on her waist.

Suddenly, just when it seemed that the entire carousel would snap and break apart like a child's toy, the music began to slow, then the platform . . . and, finally, Jennifer's heart.

As unexpectedly as it had begun, it was over. David and Vali, white-faced, turned to Jennifer and Dan. The four of them stayed frozen in place for seconds after everything had come to a halt, not speaking, barely breathing.

It was Vali who finally broke the strained silence. "Please . . . let's get out of here."

The sound of her voice roused the others into action. Dan helped Jennifer slide from her horse, pulling her against him for a moment. Gently, he touched her cheek. "Are you OK?" he whispered into her tangled hair. "You're not hurt?"

"I'm . . . fine," Jennifer said, her voice trembling. "I just want to get off, Daniel."

She clung to him as they left the ride and walked into the midst of the curious, stunned bystanders who stood murmuring among themselves.

Vali waited with them while David and one of the other riders questioned the red-haired carousel operator. When David finally returned, his face was ashen and taut with controlled anger. "He says he has no idea what happened. Someone sent a message that he was to come to the office. The fellow who brought him the message offered to stay until he got back. But he was gone by the time the ride operator returned."

Dan's expression was skeptical, but he said nothing.

On the way to the exit, the day now spoiled, Jennifer's mind raced. She couldn't shake the feeling that there was a connection between the strange-looking man in the dark suit and the malfunction of the carousel.

Vali hadn't said a word since leaving the ride. She continued to lean heavily on David, her face chalk white. With a worried aside, Jennifer suggested to Dan that they follow the other couple to their car before going to their own.

When they reached David's sleek black Corvette, the composer turned to them, releasing Vali long enough to shake hands with Daniel. "Thanks for sharing your day with us—I hope it wasn't a total loss for you." His face was granite hard with tension.

"We enjoyed being with you," Dan assured him. "Vali, are you all right?" he asked after a slight pause.

Vali didn't answer but simply hugged her arms a little more tightly to herself. David's eyes never left her face as he slipped an arm back around her shoulder.

Before they parted, Jennifer decided to tell the others about the man she'd seen at the *Magnum* and then again at the carousel.

"He kept staring at Vali," Jennifer continued. "And it was . . . an unpleasant look. Almost a . . . frightening look."

David's face paled. "What did he look like?" His mouth thinned to a hard, tight line, and his whispering voice sounded harsher than usual.

As Jennifer went on to describe the worrisome stranger, she saw Vali lift her head with an astonished look. For a moment the singer seemed about to say something, but finally she dropped her gaze away, remaining silent.

David, too, had a peculiar, stricken expression on his face. As soon as Jennifer ended her description, he said a hurried good-bye and helped Vali into the passenger's seat, then hurried to the driver's side and slid behind the wheel.

Jennifer had the impression that the enigmatic composer could hardly wait to leave the parking lot. Neither he nor Vali looked back as he drove away.

Shivering, she reached for Dan, urging him to hurry as they started for their own car.

SEVEN

E ARLY the next morning, Dan sat on the porch of their cottage in a lawn chair, enjoying the cool air and the sounds coming in off the lake. He could tell by the slapping of the waves that it was choppy this morning, and he found himself wishing he could see again, could stand along the shore and watch the sea gulls play over the breakers. From somewhere down the beach a dog barked, and beside him, Sunny made a low, answering growl of her own.

Hearing footsteps, Dan sat up a little straighter. Sunny stirred and uttered a perfunctory little bark.

"Morning, Daniel. If you're not the picture of a contented, happy man, I never saw one."

"Hi, David, you're out and about early."

"I like to walk the beach when it's like this. You can almost smell fall in the air."

At Dan's invitation, David sat down on the porch step. "I thought I'd stop and make sure you and Jennifer are both all right. I know your day at Cedar Point wasn't exactly what you'd hoped for."

"We're fine," Dan said easily. "Jennifer is inside getting dressed. Her hair dryer went on the fritz this morning, so we're going to try to track down a discount store later."

He reached over to rub Sunny's ears, and the retriever gradually settled back into her comfortable slouch again.

"How's Vali?" Dan asked. "Have you talked with her this morning?"

"Only by phone. I'm going to stop by for a few minutes before I leave. Actually, that's another reason I wanted to see you. I was wondering if I could ask a small favor of you and Jennifer. I hate to keep imposing, but—"

Dan made a quick dismissing motion with his hand. "You're not imposing. Did you say you're leaving?" He took a sip of coffee, then set his cup on the table beside him. "Would you like some coffee? There's plenty."

"No, thanks. I'm sure I'll have more than my limit later on today," he said. "I have a meeting with a producer and some other people in Nashville this evening. I plan to be back early tomorrow, but I'm a little concerned about Vali. I was wondering if you and Jennifer would mind giving her a call later today—just to check on her."

"Sure, we'd be glad to. You think she's still upset about yesterday?"

David didn't answer right away.

"Jennifer was afraid she might have made things worse for Vali by describing the man she saw at the rides," Dan ventured.

"I don't know," the composer replied. "Vali isn't . . . very strong. Emotionally, I mean. She's had . . . some problems."

"I hoped that was all behind her," Dan said carefully. "I had heard that she had a difficult time after Paul Alexander's death, but that was three years ago."

Dan heard the frustration in David's deep sigh as he shifted restlessly on the step. "Most of the time Vali seems all right. But it doesn't take much to shake her. She was badly frightened last night. I couldn't get her to talk to me at all until this morning. Now she's trying to laugh it off, but I'm not all that comfortable with leaving her alone today."

"Vali said Graham was out of town, too. Is he still gone?"

"Yes," David rasped shortly. "He won't be back until sometime tomorrow."

"Well, we'll be happy to check on her. Jennifer will be glad for a chance to say hello."

"Thanks, Dan—I really appreciate it." David paused. "Your Jennifer is a very special lady."

Dan smiled. "Yes, she surely is."

"Have you known each other for a long time?"

"Not really. I hired her as my exec at the radio station the first of the year and proceeded to fall head over heels in love with her." He hesitated. "What about you, David? Do you have someone special in your life?"

The musician didn't answer for a moment. When he did, his whisper-voice was softer than ever. "Not . . . exactly." After a slight pause, he added, "Just . . . high hopes."

"Vali?"

"It's that obvious?"

"Jennifer is always on the lookout for romance. She's hard to fool." Dan couldn't stop a smile at the thought of his wife's quick mind and inquisitive nature.

"Well . . . the competition is pretty tough, I'm afraid."

"Graham Alexander?"

"He's a rather formidable opponent."

"They're not engaged, are they? Jennifer said she didn't notice Vali wearing a ring."

"Not yet. But Graham is giving it his best shot."

Dan shrugged and lifted his eyebrows. "Until she's wearing a ring—until the wedding itself, in fact—you've still got a chance."

"Not much of one, I'm afraid." David sounded discouraged. "Graham has a definite edge on me. You see, Vali feels enormously indebted to him."

Dan frowned. "Why is that?"

"You know that Graham is Paul Alexander's twin?"

Dan nodded.

"Well, after his brother died, Graham more or less made himself responsible for Vali's welfare. You see, Vali had a complete breakdown after Paul's death."

Dan heard David get up and step down off the porch.

"All I know is what I've been told by others," he continued, "but it's common knowledge that Vali fell apart emotionally. She wouldn't sing, wouldn't eat, wouldn't see anyone—wouldn't even go out of the house, I understand."

"She's obviously better." Dan reached for his coffee cup, then felt for the pot to pour himself a refill.

"Oh, yes, she definitely is," David quickly agreed. "Though I'd like to see her a lot . . . stronger. More secure about herself, at least. At any rate," he continued, "she attributes her present . . . well-being . . . to Graham."

"I don't understand."

The composer hesitated. "Apparently Graham and his mother brought Vali up here after her . . . breakdown. They saw to it that she got excellent care in a mental health center for several months. After that, she lived with Leda—that's Graham's mother—for a few weeks until she moved into her own place here on the beach. Both Leda and Graham seem to have appointed themselves her guardians—not in the legal sense, but certainly in every other way. Graham in particular keeps a very watchful eye on Vali."

Dan could hear the undercurrent of resentment in David's words. "It sounds as if he might have been fond of her when she was still engaged to his brother," he said thoughtfully.

"No, not at all," David replied. "From what Vali's told me, she and Graham barely knew one another until after the airplane crash. She and Leda had spent some time together, and I think they became close right from the beginning. But that wasn't the case with her and Graham. Anyway," he went on, "all that

48

changed after Paul died. Now Vali seems to feel an extraordinary
sense of gratitude toward Graham. In fact—" he paused for an
instant— "I suppose this will sound like nothing more than jeal-
ousy, but I get the feeling that Graham Alexander has fostered a
kind of unhealthy dependency in Vali."

"A dependency on *him,* you mean."

"Yes. I think he has managed to convince Vali that she can't
function without him, that she's . . . helpless . . . on her own."

Dan had his doubts about the musician's theory, but he kept
them to himself. "Why would someone with Vali Tremayne's talent and reputation get involved in a relationship like that?"

"It's just a hunch," said David, "but I think Graham somehow
discovered Vali's weakness and capitalized on it. You see, she has
this incredibly distorted sense of her own worth. At some time in
her life, her self-image was virtually destroyed—or maybe it never
developed. As illogical as it may seem, considering who she is—
and how special she is—Vali has absolutely no self-confidence. I
think she's probably the most insecure person I've ever known."

Troubled, Dan thought about this as he traced the rim of his
coffee cup with his thumb. "Yet, Vali's a Christian."

"Vali was also an orphan," David replied. "Apparently she was
tossed around from one foster home to another for years. I'm convinced that's at the heart of her problems. She loves the Lord with
all her heart, and in her own way she has a close walk with him.
But she has no real understanding of God's love for *her,* as an individual." He paused, then added, "I imagine we both know Christians who have been spiritually crippled because they're unable
either to understand or to accept their own worth in God's eyes.
With Vali, I'm afraid it's become a severe emotional problem."

Dan was quiet for a long time. "She must trust you a great deal
to confide in you as she has," he finally said.

"A lot of what I know about Vali I learned from other people,"
David explained. "But, yes, she *has* shared some things about her

past with me. The rest . . . well, I care so much about her, I think I just somehow sense her feelings."

"Does she know you're in love with her?" Dan asked gently.

"I'm afraid I haven't done very well at hiding it."

"It could be that you're just what she needs to break this . . . *dependency* . . . on Graham Alexander."

"Naturally, I'd like to think so." David gave a small, harsh laugh. "But I don't have much time left, I'm afraid."

"Why? Because of your other contracts?"

"Other contracts?" David repeated. "Oh—well, yes. The agreement was that Vali and I would work together for a few weeks, then she'd make a decision about returning to her career. But in the meantime, I have recording commitments of my own to honor, and soon I'll have to go back to Nashville to stay. My time is running out."

"But you could still see her—"

"If I can't convince Vali to pick up the pieces of her career while I'm cloistered with her for hours every day, I certainly can't hope to when I'm hundreds of miles away from her." He stopped. "Yet I can't let Graham Alexander win!"

"That almost sounds like a war," Dan said mildly.

The composer was silent for a long time. Dan could hear the strain in his whisper-voice when he finally replied. "In a way, it is. But I happen to believe it's a war worth fighting."

"In a war, David, someone always gets hurt," Dan pointed out gently. "And someone always loses."

"Yes, I know," the musician whispered. "But I can promise you this, Daniel. Whatever happens, I intend to make sure that Vali isn't the one who gets hurt."

After the composer had walked away, Dan bent forward in his chair and propped his elbows on his knees. He thought about everything David had told him, puzzled by his conflicting impressions of the man.

Being blind made it difficult to "read" another person, although he had become reasonably adept at gauging the emotional barometers of those around him. It suddenly occurred to him, however, that even if he could see David's face, he quite possibly wouldn't know any more about the enigmatic musician than he already did. A deep-seated but growing doubt about the man made Dan wonder if anyone had ever seen the true face of David Nathan Keye.

EIGHT

THE man shifted his tall frame inside the phone booth, keeping one eye on the highway a few feet away.

"That fiasco at Cedar Point was incredibly stupid! What in the world possessed you? And to go yourself—"

The voice on the other end of the phone sighed with exaggerated patience. "I believe I've already explained that we simply meant to assist you with your plan. It was all quite safe."

"It was foolish, not safe!" the man snarled. "The only thing you accomplished was to make the Kaine woman suspicious."

"What do you mean?" The voice hardened.

"She *saw* you, that's what I mean. She saw you *twice,* as a matter of fact. And when I talked to Vali this morning, she was more on edge than ever."

"Then the day was a success. You need her disoriented, do you not?"

"I don't need her watching her shadow!"

"You're allowing your anxiety to distract you from the fact that all this is working to our advantage."

The man pulled at his shirt collar. "Listen to me. I know what I'm doing. If you'll just stay out of it and give me the time I need, I can tie up all the loose ends once and for all."

The voice sighed again. "Time is becoming of extreme importance, my friend. We've been patient with your infatuation with the Tremayne woman and your insistence that you can effectively silence her. But the truth is—"

"I told you—"

"The truth is," the voice interrupted with an icy note of warning, "that you're not much further along with your plan today than you were when we started. Now, we both know there's a good possibility that the singer could put us—and a number of other people, important people—behind bars for the rest of our natural lives. In addition," he pressed on in an even, cold tone, "the unfortunate return of her memory of certain events could prove disastrous to a project it has taken years to implement. That cannot be allowed. The Tremayne woman is to be neutralized. Your way, if you can accomplish it within five more days." He paused, drew a deep breath, and added quietly, *"Our* way, if not. Is that clear?"

"Perfectly clear," the man grated resentfully. "What about the others?"

"Don't give the other couple—the Kaines, is it?—a second thought. If they should turn out to be a problem or complicate our plans in any way, they're entirely expendable. We'll take care of them."

NINE

THE evening was warm, the lake calm, the breeze gentle. Dan and Jennifer strolled leisurely along the beach, his right arm resting lightly around her shoulders, his other hand gripping Sunny's harness. They walked in contented silence, Daniel smiling softly to himself as he allowed his thoughts free rein. In his usual manner, he prayed as he walked, sometimes silently, sometimes in a soft murmur.

He knew it would surprise most people to learn that he counted himself a peaceful, happy man. The reason for his peace was his relationship with a God of unconditional love and endless mercies. The reason for his happiness was the woman walking closely at his side.

How she had changed his life . . . sweetened it, enriched it, given it a meaning and an ongoing joy he would have once not dared to hope for. And these days at the beach had been glorious. . . .

Abruptly, his smile faded as an unbidden memory surfaced, bringing with it a wrenching pain. All too clearly he remembered another evening walk along a beach, this one in Florida. It hadn't been a happy time, that summer after the automobile accident that had blinded him. In truth, it had been one of the most difficult times of his life. Gabe Denton, his closest friend, had insisted that Dan put the radio station under temporary management and get away—away from home, from work, and from as many of the painful memories as possible. Dan had reluctantly given in to Gabe's urging, and together they had spent two months in a rented house on a private beach near Fort Myers.

Loneliness had tormented him like a viper that summer, poisoning him with discouragement and fear . . . the fear that he would spend the rest of his life without sight, without love, without hope . . . that he would grow old alone, never knowing the companionship or joy of having a wife and family. One particular evening, he and Gabe had walked for hours in silence along the deserted beach, neither of them able to voice each other's private dread. For one brief, desolate moment, Dan had felt an almost overwhelming urge to simply walk into the sea and let it take him.

Even years after he had finally made peace with God about the blindness, the awful loneliness had still lingered, sometimes threatening to break him. Too many times he had experienced the unsighted person's dilemma of feeling alone in the midst of a crowd, even among his own family—cut off, isolated, a solitary man in a lonely world.

But then . . . then Jennifer had come sweeping into his life, into his heart. Jennifer, his sweet, gate-crashing rebel, with her wild, wonderful mane of hair that smelled like sunshine and her honeyed voice that warmed his soul. Jennifer, with the laugh that shattered his doubts, the touch that melted his senses, and the love that had vanquished his fear of loneliness and set him free—free to love her.

Oh, my Lord . . . my loving, gracious Lord, how can I ever, ever thank you enough for her?

Hearing Daniel's soft murmur of praise, Jennifer smiled up at his profile. "What are you thinking about?"

"Just counting my blessings, darlin' . . . again," he said with the love-touched smile that was reserved for her alone.

She wrapped her arm around his waist and hugged him tightly. "We have a lot of them to count, don't we, Daniel?"

"Indeed we do, love. Indeed we do."

"Do you ever feel . . . almost guilty? Because we're so happy and other people aren't?"

"No," Dan replied without hesitation. "Just extremely grateful." He paused. "What prompted that question?"

"Oh, I don't know." She poked at a mound of sand with the toes of her bare foot. "When I see someone like Vali Tremayne, I feel almost ashamed that I can be so happy when she's so miserable."

Dan stopped. "Do you really think she's that unhappy?"

"Yes," Jennifer replied without hesitation. "I think she's *terribly* unhappy, Daniel. And I wish there were something we could do about it."

"I'm afraid all we can do right now is what David asked us to do," he said, gently squeezing her shoulder. "Let's walk over to Vali's cottage and make sure she's OK. The rest we'll have to leave to the Lord."

Vali called the cat one more time, then turned to leave the beach and go inside. She stopped when she saw Dan and Jennifer approaching from the other direction, waved, and waited as they drew near.

She was genuinely glad to see them. She liked Jennifer Kaine more than any other woman she had ever met—except for Leda, perhaps. And she thought Jennifer liked *her,* too.

Vali had never had a close woman friend, even in college. She had been far too shy back then to make any gesture of friendship on her own. Later, after she and Paul had become successful as a team in the Christian music industry, she hadn't felt the need for anyone in her life except him. Paul had often encouraged her to make friends with some of the other young women they met in their profession, but Vali had never been comfortable initiating any kind of relationship.

After Paul's death, she hadn't wanted anyone. Leda had been there, of course, and Vali owed the older woman a great deal. But Leda was more a mother figure than a friend, more a source of strength than someone to share with on a mutual level.

Now, as she saw the open friendliness on Jennifer's face, she wished there could be more time to get to know her—and Daniel, too. They made her feel wanted, and they made her feel . . . special. For the most part, she was unacquainted with both feelings.

"Hi, Vali!" Jennifer called warmly. "You going for a walk, too?"

"I've already been. Actually, I've been trying to find my run-away cat again."

Daniel laughed. "Does Trouble ever stay home where she belongs?"

"Not very often, I'm afraid. At least, I seem to spend an awful lot of time trying to track her down."

"Are you worried about her?" Jennifer asked.

"Oh, no," Vali said, waving off the suggestion. "She'll show up before long, once she realizes it's past dinnertime." She glanced from Jennifer to Dan. "You two look like you got some sun today."

"And a few new freckles," Jennifer said, rubbing the tip of her nose. "We spent most of the day on the beach. Daniel, of course, just keeps turning darker and darker, but I feel a little pink in places."

"It was a good day to get a burn," Vali agreed, "but I hope it doesn't stay this warm all night. My air conditioner isn't working right, and I haven't been able to get a repairman yet this week."

After a few more minutes of exchanging small talk, Dan and Jennifer left her and walked on down the beach. Vali called

Trouble one more time, then gave up and went inside. She had left a table light on before going on her search, and now she went to turn on the hanging lamp behind the piano as well.

She had drawn the drapes long before dark. Vali had always hated the darkness. Even after she went to bed she always left a lamp burning in the cottage. It had been Paul who had finally helped her understand her fear, which Vali knew bordered on nyctophobia. Alice Carter, one of the many foster "mothers" in her past, had often "disciplined" Vali by locking her in a small, dark, and mildewy basement under the kitchen. When her behavior was deemed particularly unacceptable, Vali had been made to stay there, alone and terrified, throughout the night.

Vali found herself wondering if her own fear of the dark had in any way contributed to her empathy for Daniel Kaine and his blindness. She shuddered at the thought of what Daniel must endure every day of his life.

Sinking down onto the sofa, she reached for the newspaper, then decided to fix some iced tea before settling in for the evening.

On the way through the small dinette between the living room and the kitchen, she stooped to retrieve one of Trouble's yarn balls. As she straightened, she caught a glimpse of something not quite right in the direction of the kitchen. She took a step, then froze. Holding her breath, she stared into the gaping blackness of the open back door.

The skin on her forearms tightened as she fought to control her fear. *Someone had been in her cottage.* She was positive she had locked the door before going outside. Someone had come into her home, boldly leaving the door open behind him.

Where was he now?

An involuntary image flashed through her mind, rocking her with panic. *The man at the Ferris wheel.* The man Jennifer had seen at the roller coaster and again at the carousel. The man with the cold, malevolent eyes.

She shook her head to banish his face from her mind. What had made her think of him?

Had he been the one watching her cottage earlier in the summer? Vali tensed even more, remembering the faceless figure who had stood outside in the darkness several weeks ago, never revealing himself, never approaching her. Simply . . . watching. She had convinced herself it was only her imagination. But what if . . .

What if he were here, inside the cottage?

Don't panic. Breathe . . . take a deep breath . . . stay calm.

No. If anyone was inside the house, he would have shown up before now. She was being childish. She was alone in the cottage; she was sure of it.

She had to shut the back door. Finally, carefully, she forced herself to take one tentative step at a time until she was standing in the middle of the kitchen.

Should she turn on the light? Her instincts told her to flood the room with brightness; still she hesitated.

Vali stared at the door for what seemed an interminable length of time before she could finally bring herself to slam it shut and throw the bolt.

Shaking, she leaned against the door, bracing her hand against the wood as she drew a long, steadying breath.

Now what?

Slowly, reluctantly, she turned around. She knew she had to search the cottage.

If only David hadn't gone away . . . or if Graham were here.

Startled by the realization that she'd thought of David first, Vali quickly turned her thoughts away from him. *Graham . . . it's Graham I need, Graham I want, not David.*

But Graham wasn't here. He was still in Cleveland. And David had gone to Nashville.

She had to do *something*. With one more deep breath, she began fumbling along the wall for the light switch. Finding it, she flipped on the light, blinked, and waited.

There was no sound, no sign of movement. Nothing.

She had to search the rest of the cottage. The living room was safe; she had just come from there. That left only her bedroom and the small bath.

On impulse, Vali opened the silverware drawer and took out a butcher knife. It could be used against her by an intruder lurking somewhere in the darkness, but it made her feel more secure.

Gripping the handle, she crossed the narrow hallway to her bedroom. The room was dark, shadowed, oppressively quiet. She took a step, heard something, backed off, and waited.

Silence.

Once again she took a hesitant step into the room, then another. Unable to stand the darkness any longer, she groped her way toward the nightstand by the bed and with trembling fingers switched on the lamp.

The lively garden colors and splashes of floral prints scattered throughout the room sprang to life, giving her a reassuring sense of normalcy. She swallowed against the sour taste of fear in her mouth. So far so good. But if someone were hiding in here, where would he be?

Under the bed, her mind answered. *Or in the closet.*

Gripping the knife, Vali dropped down on all fours and flipped back the bedspread. Her heart pounded wildly as she peered into the dim recesses under the bed.

Nothing. Nothing but a few dust bunnies and one of Trouble's yarn balls.

She breathed a sigh of relief and got to her feet.

Then she heard the noise again—behind her, in the closet. She whirled around.

A soft *thud,* then another. Vali's hand went up to her mouth, clenching into a tight, defensive fist.

Someone was in the closet. What if she hadn't heard the noise until later? She would have come into the room, undressed for her shower, gone into the adjoining bathroom, and then . . .

She had to get out of the cottage!

But what was he waiting for? He'd had any number of opportunities to grab her by now.

What did he want?

Vali suddenly remembered the knife in her hand. She glanced at it, then raised her eyes to the door of the closet.

She began to walk. Carefully, quietly, slowly.

She stopped once, then went on.

Something scraped at the door, louder now, more insistent.

He was baiting her, teasing her, playing games with her. . . .

She reached for the doorknob, paused, then yanked the door open, jumping back as it slammed against the wall.

Finally she stepped closer, the knife held high as she peered into the darkness of the closet. Her eyes searched the shadows between the clothes, up to the shelves, then down at the floor.

Suddenly something lunged at her with a screech, and Vali screamed.

TEN

HORROR gave way to incredulous relief as Vali stared down at the small gray-and-white ball of fur now wrapping itself eagerly around her ankles, humming in a low, welcoming purr.

"Trouble!"

The knife fell from her hand, clattering onto the wooden floor. The cat jumped, darted an accusing look at her owner, then raced from the room.

Vali didn't know whether to laugh or cry. Relief continued to pour over her as she stood shaking, as much from a sense of her own foolishness as from her earlier panic.

She went into the living room, where she found Trouble huddled under the piano bench, watching her. "Bad kitty!" Vali scolded, but only halfheartedly. She was too relieved to be angry with her small companion.

She was positive now that she had simply left the back door unlocked. One of Trouble's favorite tricks was to insert a paw in the space underneath a door and pry until the door opened. Obviously, the cat had let herself in.

With a rueful smile, Vali remembered other times the kitten had maneuvered herself into a closet or a room using the same trick.

But could she have shut the closet door behind her?

Vali glanced back toward the bedroom. It was possible, she reassured herself. Trouble was always doing things other cats never seemed to think of.

But shutting a closet door?

Determined to shake off the unease still plaguing her, Vali went back to the couch and sat down. She was no longer in the mood to read, so she reached for the television's remote control.

Unexpectedly, the telephone beside the couch rang. Vali jumped, stared at the phone for a moment, then lifted the receiver.

"You should be more careful about locking your doors, Vali."

The voice was a harsh, unpleasant whisper. Startled, Vali jerked the receiver away from her ear, staring at it as though it were a snake about to strike.

She waited, drawing in a long breath before lifting the receiver to her ear again.

"Don't worry about it, Vali. I'm going to be looking after you tonight . . . *all* night. I'll be right there with you."

Vali's throat seemed paralyzed. She tried to speak but could only choke out a strangled sob.

"Be sure to keep your doors locked until I get there, Vali. But don't worry about waiting up for me. I'll let myself in . . . just as I did earlier. By the way, did you ever find that troublesome cat of yours?"

Vali slammed down the receiver, her entire body shaking violently.

The phone rang almost immediately.

She covered her ears with her hands, staring at the telephone in horror.

The phone went on ringing for a full two minutes before it stopped, leaving an ominous silence in the cottage.

Vali looked around the room, then went to the large picture window. She edged the drapes back enough to peer out, but saw nothing. Suddenly she remembered the broken air conditioner—and the open bedroom window.

As she was on her way to the bedroom, the telephone started ringing again.

Frantic, she ran into the bedroom, cranked the casement window shut, and locked it.

The phone was still ringing.

Her back to the wall, Vali stood staring numbly through the open doorway, across the hall into the living room.

Make it stop, Lord . . . please make it stop. . . .

Finally there was silence. Vali pushed away from the wall and went to check the kitchen window, then the door, even though she had locked it only minutes earlier.

She had to think. She stood in the middle of the kitchen, then remembered the small jalousie window in the bathroom and hurried back across the hall to check it.

The kitten trailed behind her, curious and wanting to play. She pounced at Vali's feet and ran between her legs, tripping her. "Stop it, Trouble!" Vali screamed, and the cat fled back to the living room.

The front door . . . had she locked it?

She went to check and found both the lock and the dead bolt secure.

No one could get in. She was safe.

Unless they wanted in badly enough to break a window.

Should she turn out the lights?

No. He might think she'd gone to bed. She wanted him to know she was awake and watching. Besides, she couldn't spend the rest of the night in the dark. She would go crazy.

She had to call the police. Now.

The jangle of the telephone made every muscle in her body go into spasms again.

She yanked the receiver off the hook. *"Stop it!"* she screamed.

"I hope you've found your naughty kitten by now, Vali. I put her in the closet for you so she couldn't run away again. You have such pretty things in your closet, Vali. I especially like the pink silk dress. It's real silk, isn't it? It must feel cool and soft against your skin."

Sobbing, Vali threw the receiver against the table.

Then the lights went out.

Vali panicked, cried out, then dropped to the floor, crouching in a terrified huddle against the back of the couch. Her pulse was out of control, her breathing labored in the inky darkness.

Trouble came padding noiselessly over to her, nuzzling Vali's clenched hands and purring softly as she pressed her small head into her owner's lap.

Call someone while you still can . . . call the police.

She wouldn't be able to see the number in the dark. . . .

Try to find it . . . call the Kaines . . . call Leda.

Yes! She knew Leda's number by heart. She would call her, and Leda would send the police.

She began to crawl around the couch, fumbling for the receiver. It was dangling over the side of the table. She got to her feet, grasping the receiver with a shaking hand.

The phone was dead.

Now she was completely cut off from any hope of help. She was alone. Alone in the dark.

She picked up the telephone, yanked it out of the wall connection, and hurled it across the room.

Something moved outside, close to the wall of the cottage. Then something snapped, as if someone had stepped on a branch.

Vali whipped around.

The knife . . . what had she done with the knife?

Something began to scrape softly at the screened window, slowly, then faster, rougher, louder. The scraping gave way to a brutal pounding against the outside wall. The banging grew louder and more frenzied, until the very walls seemed to shake.

Vali backed away, her gaze riveted on the wall. Slowly she slid down the wall, her hands covering her ears, as she sobbed in mute appeal.

The pounding went on and on. Even with her ears tightly covered, Vali could still hear it, could feel the vibrations, her body shaking with every *thud*.

She screamed once more in desperation, then sat huddled weakly against the wall, waiting.

Help me . . . oh, please, please, help me. . . .

ELEVEN

J ENNIFER set a cup of hot tea on the table in front of Vali. "Drink this, Vali," she urged softly. "Is there anything else I can get for you?"

Vali shook her head and squinted against the morning sunshine. She lifted the cup with a trembling hand, spilling some of the tea before it reached her lips.

Sunny stirred restlessly as Dan drummed his fingers on the table—the only sound in the kitchen. Jennifer had a fleeting, unpleasant sensation of the stillness of a house after a death. It was as if, given the extraordinary circumstances of the night before, an ordinary level of noise would have been intolerable.

Graham Alexander stood directly behind Vali, his hands resting protectively on her shoulders. His mother sat beside Vali, studying the younger woman's face with maternal concern, absently patting her hand from time to time in a reassuring gesture.

Leda Alexander had been a surprise to Jennifer. The Greek-born novelist looked to be in her early fifties. She was short and attractive, with dark hair and olive-toned skin. Instead of the cosmopolitan sophisticate Jennifer had expected, the internationally acclaimed novelist was slightly overweight and plainly dressed, and gave off an unaffected air of common sense and comfort. Her warm smile and direct manner had immediately put Jennifer at ease. Without question, she found Graham's mother far easier to like than her son.

Jennifer had to admit, however, that Graham's concern seemed genuine enough. "We're deeply indebted to you and your wife, Mr. Kaine," he was saying. "If you hadn't been worried enough to come over here last night and check on Vali, there's no telling what might have happened."

Dan quickly dismissed the man's gratitude with a slight shake of his head. "I'm just sorry we had to break down Vali's door. But as we explained to her last night, when she didn't answer the phone, we had the operator check her line; we were almost certain she was here. When the operator said the line was out of order, we thought we should make sure she was all right."

Jennifer drew up a chair beside Dan, continuing where he left off. "We were just so worried about you, Vali. And when you didn't come to the door, I really got scared. We were afraid you might be hurt and need help. That's when Daniel decided to break in."

Vali finally spoke, her voice halting and uncertain. "Please, Daniel . . . don't apologize again for the door. I don't know what I would have done if . . . you hadn't come when you did. I'm so grateful to you . . . and to Jennifer . . . for taking me back to your cottage."

"Yes, that was awfully kind of you," Leda Alexander put in. "And I can't thank you enough for calling us first thing this morning."

"But Vali . . . dear . . ." Jennifer looked up to find Graham Alexander frowning down at Vali. "What I don't understand is why you didn't simply answer the door when the Kaines arrived."

Jennifer saw Vali tense even more.

"I told you, Graham, I—I suppose I must have panicked. I was terrified by then!"

Graham nodded his head knowingly, darting an "I told you so" glance at his mother.

Leda, however, seemed unaware of her son's pointed look. "Of course you were, darling. Anyone would have been."

Graham sounded less convinced. "But surely you recognized Mr. Kaine's—*Daniel's*—voice, dear."

Vali darted an embarrassed glance at Dan and Jennifer. "I should have . . . I know . . . but I was so frightened. . . ."

Graham nodded with no apparent conviction, patting her gently on top of her head as though she were an unreliable child. "It's all right, dear. We understand."

Jennifer was surprised to see anger spark in Vali's eyes as she turned to look at him. "No, I don't think you do, Graham! You weren't here—you couldn't possibly know what it was like for me!"

The scientist lifted a disapproving eyebrow but said nothing.

"I didn't *imagine* it, Graham!"

"Vali," Graham's mother quickly interrupted, "Graham knows that. He's just concerned for you, darling. We both are. Now—" she squeezed Vali's hand and smiled at her— "I want you to throw some things in your overnighter. You can spend a few days with me until the police get this awful thing straightened out."

Vali looked at Leda uncertainly. "I don't know, Leda . . . I don't think—"

"Mother's right, Vali," Graham said firmly. "You can't possibly stay here until we get the door repaired and the police take care of—this other business."

"But Graham, I don't want—"

"Vali? You in here?"

Without waiting for a reply, David Nathan Keye walked in, stopping in the doorway of the kitchen. In one hand he held a bouquet of rosebuds wrapped in green floral paper.

His dark gray eyes took in each person in the room for an instant before finally coming to rest on Vali.

"Well," David said, "I was about to wish you a happy birthday, but it looks as if the party's already begun. What happened to the front door?"

Jennifer turned to Vali. "Today is your birthday? And you haven't said a word!"

David crossed the room and, with a low bow and a wide, sweeping motion, presented the bouquet to Vali. "Happy birthday, Princess."

Jennifer looked at Graham Alexander, whose features had tightened to a hard, unpleasant mask.

David, too, flicked an indifferent glance at the scientist, then greeted Leda with what appeared to be genuine warmth. Finally he returned his attention to Vali.

"Thank you, David," she said softly, pushing her chair away from the table and starting to rise. "I'll put these in water."

But Leda Alexander stopped her with a restraining hand. "I'll do it, darling. You rest." Getting to her feet, she stopped for a moment to give David a peculiar look. "Vali had some trouble here last night. She's terribly upset."

The composer dropped to one knee beside Vali. "What kind of trouble? What happened?"

Graham answered for Vali. "I don't think Vali needs to go into the details again," he said coldly. "It will only make it more difficult for her."

David ignored him. "Vali?" he prompted, covering her hand with his own.

Vali glanced up at Graham, then turned back to David. "Someone . . . someone was in the cottage last night."

"What?" The composer's mouth went hard.

Vali described to him then, in her soft, hesitant voice, the events of the night before. When she was done, David gently released her hand and stood.

"You've called the police?" David asked, looking at Graham.

The scientist bristled. "Of course we called the police," he answered caustically. "They've already been here. When you arrived, we were about to help Vali get some of her things packed so she can spend a few days with my mother."

David looked from Graham to Vali. "Is that what you want to do, Princess?"

"I . . . I suppose," Vali said, not meeting David's gaze but instead staring woodenly down at her lap. As she spoke, she hugged her arms tightly against her body. "I can't stay here until the door is fixed."

David nodded and once again dropped down beside her. "Is there anything I can do, Vali? Any way I can help?"

Jennifer's throat tightened at the way the composer's gaze went over Vali's face. *He adores her,* she realized. *He truly does love her.*

The thought gave her no satisfaction. She still felt a sense of apprehension about Keye, in spite of his undeniable charm and apparent devotion to Vali. It puzzled her, how she could like him— and she did—yet at the same time not completely trust him.

It occurred to her that Vali might be better off without *either* of the two men who seemed so intent on claiming her affection. David Nathan Keye made Jennifer uncomfortable; she couldn't quite shake the feeling he was hiding something. As for Graham Alexander—well, she simply didn't like the man. Not a very Christian sentiment, but there it was. She thought him cold, arrogant, and decidedly overbearing.

The scientist's frosty, precise voice abruptly pierced her thoughts. "Vali said you were out of town, David. When, exactly, did you return?"

The composer glanced up at Alexander, studying him for a long moment. "I was in Nashville, Graham. And I returned just this morning." He got to his feet, his eyes glinting with challenge. "Why do you ask?"

Graham Alexander scrutinized the musician with a raking stare.

"The man who called Vali last night spoke in what she described as a . . . hoarse whisper."

The underlying accusation hung tensely between them. No one spoke as the two men glared at each other. David's face was ashen, but he continued to meet the other's look with a steady gaze of his own. "A common enough method of disguising your voice, I believe," he said. "One that's used rather frequently, I imagine."

Something flared in Graham Alexander's eyes, then subsided. He shrugged, and the tension was broken.

"Vali," Graham said solicitously, moving from behind her chair to interpose himself between her and David, "let Mother help you pack now. We need to get you settled so you can rest. I'll see to it that your door is repaired as soon as possible."

"And the phone, too," Vali reminded him.

"The phone?" David looked questioningly from Vali to Graham.

"The line was cut," Graham answered curtly.

David blanched, but he remained silent.

"Vali, darling," Leda began, "this was supposed to be a surprise, but I'm going to tell you now because there's no way I can keep it a secret all afternoon if you go home with me. Besides, I think you'll want your new friends to know."

She smiled at Dan and Jennifer, then explained, "I had planned a small party for this evening—to celebrate Vali's birthday."

"Oh, Leda—I don't want—"

"I knew you wouldn't *want*." Leda waved away Vali's objection. "That's why it was going to be a surprise. Just us, and Graham and David, of course. And Jeff Daly."

Graham gave her a clearly disapproving look. "You're still seeing him?"

His mother flushed, then countered, "As often as possible, Graham."

He pursed his lips but said nothing.

"Anyway," Leda continued, "now that you know, Vali, I thought you might like Daniel and Jennifer to come, too." She smiled at Jennifer and added, "If you can, that is."

Jennifer glanced at Dan, who seemed to sense her question. "It's up to you, love," he said.

"We wouldn't want to intrude on a family evening," Jennifer said hesitantly.

"Oh, but you wouldn't be," Leda insisted. "We'd love to have you."

"Please, Jennifer," Vali added. "I'd really like for you and Daniel to come."

"Mother, the Kaines are on their honeymoon, I believe," Graham Alexander put in. "We're making it difficult for them to refuse, but I hardly think they'd be interested in a family dinner."

Jennifer was surprised when Daniel settled the issue. "We'll be there." Rising from his chair, he added, "But I think we'd better be going now."

Jennifer got up and, after studying Vali's forlorn expression for a moment, walked over and impulsively gave her a hug. "We'll see you tonight, Vali. Try to get some rest."

She could have wept at the look of gratitude that washed over the singer's face. She wished she could just bundle Vali up and take her home with her and Daniel. She guessed Vali Tremayne to be within a year or two of her own age, and yet at times the sad young woman evoked a protective instinct in Jennifer nearly as strong as her maternal affection for little Jason.

David walked out with Dan and Jennifer, with Sunny in the lead. "I'm glad you're coming tonight," he said. "Vali's really very fond of both of you."

"She's so special," Jennifer said quickly. "I just wish last night had never happened. It must have been a nightmare for her."

"How . . . was she?" David asked hesitantly. "When you finally found her?"

Jennifer evaded his question, uncertain as to how much she ought to tell him.

But Daniel surprised her with his candor. "She was hysterical," he said quietly but with conviction. "It took at least ten minutes just to get her calmed down enough to find out what happened."

Jennifer watched Keye carefully but couldn't gauge his response to Daniel's words.

"But . . . you do believe her?" asked the composer.

"Believe her?" Daniel repeated.

"That it actually happened."

"Oh, it happened all right," Daniel replied. "She was terrified." He paused, then said even more emphatically, "Vali didn't imagine it. Someone scared her almost witless."

"And the phone lines *had* been cut, David," Jennifer reminded him.

The musician raked an unsteady hand through his already tousled hair. Jennifer suddenly noticed how weary he looked.

"David, do you have any idea who could be behind this?" asked Dan. "Has Vali been having any particular problems with someone lately? Someone who might be trying to terrorize her?"

"Vali?" David gave a short, voiceless laugh. "No, certainly not. For one thing, she's almost a recluse. She sees no one but me, Graham, and Leda, except when she goes to church—and even there, she avoids any real contact. Besides, Vali would walk a mile out of her way to avoid causing offense. No," he repeated tersely, "I can assure you that whatever is going on, it's none of Vali's doing."

Dan said nothing for a moment. When he finally spoke, his tone was faintly puzzled. "It seems to me that whoever was responsible for last night had no intention of hurting Vali. It was more a deliberate attempt to frighten her." Another thought seemed to strike him, and he added, "You know, I wouldn't be surprised if our runaway carousel wasn't the same kind of incident."

"Daniel, do you really think someone would go to that much trouble just to scare Vali?" Jennifer asked in surprise.

"I think it's possible," Daniel replied. Jennifer glanced at David Nathan Keye, disturbed by the intense gaze he had fastened on Daniel. As if the composer suddenly realized she was watching him, he looked away, whispered an abrupt good-bye, then started down the beach toward his house.

TWELVE

LEDA Alexander lived in a Gothic house right off the pages of a Victorian novel. It loomed in shrouded, mysterious dignity on a corner lot in one of Sandusky's oldest and most graciously restored neighborhoods. Jennifer took one long look at its gables and towers above the wraparound veranda and sighed longingly.

"Is that a sigh of appreciation or envy?" Dan asked as they started up the long, narrow walkway to the front door.

"Both. It's *wonderful,* Daniel! It looks like a giant dollhouse."

Before Jennifer could press the bell, the massive oak door with its stained glass panels was thrown open. Vali stood just inside, smiling warmly at the two of them.

She goes with the house, Jennifer thought.

In a flowered dress with long sleeves and a high neckline, Vali looked exquisitely feminine—and extremely young. The two men in her life had already arrived and were standing behind her, much like sentries at the castle gate.

Graham, impressively well groomed and proper as always, had exchanged his customary suit for a navy pullover and tan slacks. His polite-but-distant smile was firmly in place as Jennifer and Dan entered.

David, in a pair of white jeans and his usual striped shirt, looked comfortable but still tired, Jennifer noticed. He grinned at her, then pulled a stick of gum from his shirt pocket.

Jennifer was describing the spacious, ornate entry hall to Daniel when Leda Alexander appeared. Brushing away a smudge of flour from her nose, she dried her hands on a kitchen towel. "Where's your dog, Daniel?" she asked in her blunt, strident voice.

"We left her at the cottage. I wasn't sure whether we ought to bring her along."

"Oh, she wouldn't be a problem at all!" Leda insisted. "I should have thought to include her in the invitation. I like dogs."

"That's all right. We really can't stay too long."

"I don't think we want to hear that," the novelist said, firmly grasping his arm. "Let's go into the library. I put the snacks and punch in there." She flashed a quick smile at Jennifer before turning to guide Dan through the large double doors off the hall.

"What a wonderful room!" Jennifer exclaimed as they entered the library. A tasteful blend of fine hardwood, massive furniture, velvet drapes, and intricate cornices, the room was sumptuous with rich, deep colors of rose and gold. It apparently served as a combination study and music room. Floor-to-ceiling bookcases were filled to capacity. A concert-size ebony grand piano dominated a large space at the far end of the room, dwarfing a nearby electronic keyboard and a music cabinet.

Leda stopped at a giant sideboard heaped with a variety of snacks and two towering punch bowls. "Here, Daniel—we've arrived at the food. I'll run down the list, and you can tell me what you'd like."

Appreciating the novelist's direct, comfortable attitude toward Daniel's blindness, Jennifer offered, "I can do that, Leda. I already know without asking what he'll want."

With an interested smile, Dan inclined his head toward his wife. "Tell *me,* why don't you?"

"Well, for starters, Daniel, there's an enormous bowl of shrimp." His eyes widened, and so did his smile.

"Oh, Vali—I almost forgot." Jennifer reached in her purse

and pulled out a small gift-wrapped package. "For your birthday," she said.

With a shy word of thanks, Vali took the gift and placed it on a long library table with some others. Then, at Leda's instructions, she went to get ice for the punch, taking Graham with her to fetch the coffee urn from the kitchen.

"Leda, Leda, you made *baklava!*" David stared down at a large tray of pastry, his eyes glinting with anticipation.

"*Baklava?*" Daniel repeated.

"It's a Greek pastry," Leda explained. "Have one."

Daniel bit into one of the delicate sweets, and his face lit up with pleased surprise. "Mmm. I've never tasted anything like this. Did you make it yourself, Leda?"

"Yes. It takes forever. I used to make it more often. It was one of Paul's favorites. . . ." She stopped, glanced away for an instant, then brightened. "I'm glad you like it, Daniel. You and Jennifer can take some home with you tonight."

"I thought Jeff was coming," David said, reaching for a second pastry.

Leda glanced at the doorway Graham had just exited. "He had planned to be here, but he called about an hour ago to say he isn't going to make it. A former client is in Port Clinton, and they're having dinner tonight." She turned to Dan and Jennifer. "Jeff is my next-door neighbor," she explained. "He's an attorney."

David gave Jennifer a conspiratorial wink. "Just moved in this summer, and already he's fallen for the girl next door."

Leda colored and darted a warning look at David.

He grinned at her. "Hey—I'm cheering you on. A good man is hard to find, Leda. Go for it."

The author shook her head in hopeless resignation, but Jennifer noticed that the smile she gave David was affectionate. "Well, it will save Graham from glaring at the poor man all evening, anyway," she said wryly.

"Graham just hasn't accepted the fact," David said archly, "that his mother is still a young and attractive woman."

"That will get you all the *baklava* you want, young man," Leda said with a droll smile. She turned to Jennifer. "I think what Graham can't accept is my being interested in anyone other than his father. My husband died several years ago. Farrell was a wonderful man, but it *has* been a long time. . . ." She shook her head. "I can never predict Graham. Paul was always easier," she said with a sigh. "Graham has always been so . . . complicated. But, then, they say he's a genius. I don't suppose there's any such thing as an uncomplicated genius."

A few minutes later, Jennifer tugged at Dan's arm and led him down to the other end of the room. "This piano is magnificent, Daniel." The lid was closed, but she couldn't resist touching the top of it gently. It was obviously an instrument crafted by experts.

Leda came to stand beside them. "This was Paul's piano," she said softly. "After the accident . . . I had it brought here." She paused. "Vali says you're both familiar with Paul's music."

Daniel nodded with a sad smile. "Familiar with it—and in awe of it. If your one son is a scientific genius, your other son was a musical genius, Mrs. Alexander."

"Please—call me Leda. Yes, I think you're right about Paul—he was definitely gifted," she said with quiet pride. "He was also a good son. A fine man."

Seeing the older woman's eyes mist, Jennifer reached out to touch her arm. "It was a terrible loss for you."

Leda gave a small shake of her head. "Yes. And for many." She turned toward the opposite end of the room, where Vali stood talking with Graham.

After a moment, Leda began to herd everyone into the dining room for cake and ice cream. Two enormous sheet cakes rested in the middle of a long walnut table. One was lavishly decorated and heaped high with fresh strawberries. The other was plain, with white frosting and candy flowers.

Vali exclaimed with pleasure as she bent over the strawberry-topped cake. "Oh, Leda! It's absolutely beautiful!"

Leda laughed at her enthusiasm. "This child is positively wild about strawberries," she explained to Jennifer and Dan. "But I had to make another cake for Graham—he's allergic to them."

At Leda's request, David asked the blessing. For some reason, Jennifer wasn't surprised to catch a glimpse of Graham Alexander's look of mild scorn just before the composer began to pray.

Leda cut the strawberry cake, first handing a generous piece to Vali.

"No candles, Mother?" Graham asked.

"Oh dear, I forgot!" Leda looked flustered.

Vali laughed and reached to squeeze the older woman's shoulder. "I don't need candles! Just give me the strawberries!"

Leda cut another piece, put it on a plate, and offered it to David, who hesitated, then shook his head. "I'm afraid I'll have to share Graham's cake. I don't tolerate strawberries very well, either."

Leda raised her eyes to his face. "Well, David—so you and Graham *do* have something in common after all, even if it is only an allergy." A look of dry amusement crossed her face.

David stared at her for a moment. A hint of mischief gleamed in his eyes, and he said, "I think Graham and I have more in common than you might realize, Leda."

The novelist lifted her dark brows. "Mm. Yes, that's likely so," she agreed, glancing at her son, who stood behind Vali, looking as if his face had been chiseled from stone.

After they had eaten, Vali opened her presents. Conspicuous by its absence was a gift from Graham. Jennifer wondered about this until she saw him draw Vali to one side. "My gift for you is private, dear," he said quietly. "I'll give it to you tomorrow night at dinner, when we're alone." Vali paled at his words, appearing to be more disturbed than pleased.

It was David's gift, wrapped in a thin package resembling a stationery box, that seemed to give Vali the most pleasure.

With a puzzled smile, Vali unwrapped it and lifted a few sheets of paper from within, staring at them for a long time before finally lifting her eyes to look at David, perched on a hassock. "You wrote this for me?"

He studied her expression anxiously, then smiled at her. "With a title like *Vali's Song,* it must be for you."

They continued to stare at each other. Jennifer couldn't resist a covert glance at Graham Alexander. His face was crimson, his mouth a tight line, his eyes glazed with what could only be anger.

Leda broke the silence. "What a nice thing to do, David! But this is a gift that's meant to be shared, Vali. Won't you sing it for us, darling?"

Vali cast a startled glance at the older woman. "Oh—I don't think so. . . ."

David rose and, still smiling, closed the distance between them. He took Vali's hand, coaxing her out of her chair. "Leda's right, Princess. That magnificent voice of yours is meant to be shared." His eyes never left her face. "Sing your song for us, Vali. Please."

Everyone but Graham added their own appeal to David's. Vali hesitated. Her gaze traveled to the piano at the other end of the room. Finally, she seemed to make her decision, squaring her shoulders and giving Leda a ghost of a smile. "I haven't sung for anyone other than David for so long—"

"What better time to begin than now, when you're surrounded by people who care for you—and with a song that was written just for you?" Leda asked softly.

Gently, David urged her toward the piano, the others following.

"Will you play it for me first?" Vali asked him as he propped the lid on the piano.

David smiled at her and eased himself onto the piano bench.

When Vali would have handed him the music, he shook his head, smiling as he began humming, then running through a sampling of chord progressions with no particular pattern. He stopped once, glancing up at Leda as if a thought had just struck him. "Are you sure it isn't going to bother you—my playing Paul's piano?"

Leda met his gaze. "No, Paul allowed all his friends to use the piano. Even their children." She gave him a small, sad smile. "He always said . . . that a musical instrument was worthless when it was silent."

Jennifer saw the composer study Leda's face with a look of tenderness and understanding. Then his hands began to caress the keys with the touch of a master, finally settling into a plaintive, haunting melody. "This is your song, Vali," he said at last, the music flowing effortlessly.

At first, Vali merely scanned the music as David played. But it wasn't long before she began to sway gently with the rhythm. Soon she began to hum, then sing the words, faintly at first, then with more strength and assurance. Finally, the unforgettable voice that had made her famous began to wrap its incredible power and richness around the melody.

Jennifer clung to Daniel's hand, holding her breath as she listened to the voice that had once thrilled her on recordings. She heard Dan sigh with admiration and knew he shared her feelings.

The song was achingly beautiful, an unforgettable tribute to the singer that stopped just short, Jennifer thought, of being a love song. When it was over, there was a long silence before everyone—everyone but Graham—exploded into applause and mingled outbursts of appreciation.

Jennifer glanced at David and caught her breath at the expression on his face. She knew she would never forget the depth of emotion she saw in that look—the inexplicable pain, but most of all, the love. At that moment, Jennifer knew that, whatever else David Nathan Keye might be, he was, above all else, a man consumed by love.

Everyone begged for more, and Vali complied, although with some hesitancy at first. The longer she sang, however, the more she seemed to respond to the music. Like a rose that had been buried in the snow over a long winter, the young singer opened herself one petal at a time, revealing what seemed to be a limitless supply of ability and incredible power. Jennifer stood in dazed awe, knowing she was watching the renewal of a talent only God could have created.

She was so absorbed in the event taking place before her eyes that she was startled when Vali, still singing, wedged herself between Jennifer and Daniel and tugged them closer to the piano. David, grinning his approval, kept playing but told Dan, "Have a piano, Daniel. I'll furnish the orchestra." He then slid smoothly from the bench, at the same time guiding Dan onto it before turning to the electronic keyboard nearby.

Dan moved effortlessly into the song David had been playing without missing more than a beat.

Vali linked her arm through Jennifer's. "This act needs a little harmony, Jennifer—and your husband says you're a great singer. Help me out."

Jennifer stared at Vali in astonishment. "I couldn't sing with *you!*"

"Hey—I'm not so bad," Vali teased. "Come on, let's try."

Their banter was lost in a thundering, driving cadence from the keyboard. Dan took his cue from David, jumping quickly into the upbeat, rousing tempo of a popular contemporary number. Dumbfounded at the position she now found herself in, Jennifer nevertheless launched into the song, surprised at how easy it was for her to fall into harmony with Vali.

Wait until our folks hear about this! she thought, almost overcome with excitement.

They sang for the next twenty minutes. Jennifer, though she had originally been trained in operatic music, was an avid devotee of Christian contemporary and knew every song Vali ran by her. She didn't miss Graham Alexander's glare of disapproval throughout the entire time, but she was having too much fun to care. They stopped only once, to enjoy a friendly duel between Dan and David at their respective keyboards.

Daniel was a highly trained musician with a wealth of natural ability, and Jennifer felt herself about to explode with the pride and pleasure of watching him hold his own with one of the foremost musicians in the industry. David challenged him playfully, throwing one variation after another at him, each of which Dan met easily with an improvisation of his own. Finally, they blended their instruments together and broke into a medley of well-known praise numbers, bringing Jennifer and Vali back into the music, and ending at last with Dan and even Leda singing along.

When they were done, Leda grabbed Vali and embraced her, weeping unashamedly. "It's been so long, darling, . . . so long!"

Only Graham stood back, watching with an expression of open displeasure.

Finally David turned off the keyboard and reached to shake Dan's hand. "Daniel, you belong in the business! You're *good,* man! Really good."

Dan's smile was modest but pleased. "Thanks, but I believe I'm right where I belong. I have everything any man could ever hope for—and more." He turned his head in Jennifer's direction. "Much more."

David glanced from one to the other. "Well, I hope you'll at least keep up with your writing. Give us another *Daybreak.*"

"I didn't actually write *Daybreak* because I wanted to, David," Dan said, rising from the piano bench. "I wrote it because I *had* to. The truth is, I had never even thought of writing music. The station has been my ministry for years."

"The station and your counseling," Jennifer reminded him.

David studied Dan curiously. "What kind of counseling?"

"I just finished up a degree in Christian counseling a few weeks ago," Dan explained. "Mostly I work with the blind."

"What a full life you have, Daniel," Vali said softly. "I don't know how you manage everything."

"I don't." Dan grinned and motioned to Jennifer at his side. "She does the managing." His expression turned serious. "One thing's for sure, Vali," he said. "There can't be any doubt about *your* ministry. What an absolutely incredible gift God has given you."

At that point, Graham stepped in, wrapping his arm possessively around Vali's shoulders. "We're all aware of that, Daniel," he said stiffly. "However, the frenzied pace of her career hasn't always been . . . healthy for Vali. That's why it's so important that she take her time and not rush into anything."

Jennifer saw an expression flicker across Dan's face, but his voice revealed nothing. "I can understand that."

David, watching the exchange, flashed an impish smile at Graham. "Ah, Graham . . . ever the careful, analytical scientist. We emotional musician types must really frustrate you."

"The world needs all kinds," Graham returned smoothly.

David lifted both eyebrows in mock surprise, obviously readying his comeback.

As if she sensed a confrontation brewing, Leda broke in. "Graham, would you and David help me for a moment, please? I need to move the sideboard back into the dining room."

As soon as Leda and the two men left the room, Vali spoke up.

"Daniel—" she paused, looked at Jennifer, then went on in a soft, hesitant tone— "I was wondering . . . about your counseling. . . ."

Dan nodded, giving her a questioning smile.

"I was wondering . . . would you . . . could I . . . talk with you . . . sometime?"

Dan looked surprised. "Vali, most of my experience has been with people who are disabled in some way—particularly the blind."

Vali didn't reply immediately. When she finally spoke, her voice was low and strained. "Daniel, I *am* disabled."

Jennifer touched her lightly on the arm. "Vali, I'll leave so you can talk to Daniel."

"No," Vali protested. "Please don't." Once more she turned to Daniel. "Daniel, I need help. There's something wrong . . . with my mind, I think."

He frowned. "Why would you think that?"

"I'm afraid, Daniel. I'm afraid almost all the time! And I don't even know what I'm afraid of. I've seen doctors, . . . and I've prayed for healing. But I never seem to get any better."

Jennifer watched the frail young singer clench and then relax her hands. The contrast between the dynamic, joyful performer of a few moments before and the uncertain, faltering girl now staring up at Daniel was almost incomprehensible.

"Vali, it takes a long time before a counselor can really help," Dan said kindly. "We'll be going home in a few days."

"I know that," Vali said quickly. "But I thought perhaps you could at least—" She stopped. "I'm sorry. I can't seem to remember that the two of you are supposed to be on your honeymoon. I insist on barging into your life, don't I? I'm really sorry—please forget I said anything."

"No, Vali—that's all right." Dan's expression was troubled. "Listen, I'd be glad to talk with you. I just don't want to mislead you, that's all."

Vali stared miserably down at the floor.

"Vali—," Dan pressed gently, "will you be coming back to your cottage soon, do you think?"

"Tomorrow, I hope. If everything is repaired by then."

"When you get back, why don't you give us a call—or just come over. We'll talk, OK?"

"Are you sure, Daniel? I hate asking you, but—"

"It's perfectly all right," Dan assured her. "You're a friend. Right, Jennifer?"

Jennifer caught Vali's hand. "Daniel's right. You're not imposing at all, Vali. We want to help if we can."

She stopped, startled by Graham Alexander's sudden reappearance.

"I couldn't help but overhear part of your conversation," he said, his voice hard as he came to stand next to Vali. "I must tell you that I think this could be a very risky idea, Vali."

"Graham—please . . ."

"If you feel the need for professional help," he went on in the same cold tone, "then we should consult a physician. A specialist." He glanced at Dan with obvious pique. "I don't want to be rude or denigrate your competence, Mr. Kaine, but as you pointed out to Vali, you'll be leaving soon."

He turned back to Vali then, and Jennifer had never seen him look quite as stern as he did at that moment. "I do wish you had discussed this with me, dear."

At that moment, David walked up. "Is there any particular reason why she should have?"

Alexander bristled noticeably. "This is none of your business, Keye!"

Seemingly unruffled, David clucked his tongue and gave the other a wicked grin. "Careful, Graham. You're going to show some emotion here, if you don't watch it."

"You insolent—"

"*Stop* it!" It was Leda who put an end to the developing skirmish. "That's enough from both of you," she said sharply. "This is Vali's birthday." She turned to the composer. "David, you're a guest in my home and always a welcome one, so long as you don't upset Vali. And Graham, you may be my son, but the same thing applies to you."

The determined thrust of her chin and her steady, censuring glare silenced both men.

"I'm sorry, Leda," David offered apologetically. "You're absolutely right. I was out of line."

Graham's eyes never left the musician's face as he muttered a grudging, "Sorry, Mother." He then turned to Vali. "But I meant what I said, Vali. Your emotions are too important to toy with. If you're serious about this, there are a couple of excellent men in the area who would accept you as a patient, I'm sure."

"For heaven's sake, Graham, I don't want to commit myself to an asylum! I just want to talk with someone—another Christian, preferably—who might be able to help me sort out my problems."

Graham flinched, but his tight mask of control never slipped. After a long, awkward silence, he said, "We can talk about this tomorrow. I have to leave now; I still have notes to dictate tonight. Will you see me out?"

"I—yes, of course," Vali stammered, moving quickly toward the door without looking at anyone.

As soon as Vali returned to the room, Jennifer and Dan said their good-byes and went to the car.

Jennifer was securing her seat belt when she saw David and Vali walk out onto the porch together. He reached for her hand, said something, then released her and started down the walk toward his Corvette parked at the curb. With a brief wave in Jennifer's direction, he unlocked the car and got in.

Just before she started the car and pulled away, Jennifer looked once more at Vali standing alone on the porch. Again she felt an involuntary tug of concern. She frowned and shook her head as if to banish her increasingly strong feelings of apprehension for Vali Tremayne.

As she turned the corner and headed for the highway, she glanced in the rearview mirror to see the headlights of David's car following close behind. Again, Jennifer wondered about the composer's role in Vali's life. Was he a part of the troubled young woman's problems? Or, although she considered it highly unlikely, could he possibly be a key to the solution?

THIRTEEN

AT ELEVEN o'clock that night, a man uttered a series of curt monosyllables into his telephone receiver. He shifted impatiently in his chair, waiting for a chance to make a statement.

Finally his opportunity came. "I think we need to do something about Kaine and his wife."

There was a long pause. "I thought you said they were harmless."

"That was my first impression. But apparently he's some kind of . . . counselor." The man pulled in a deep breath in irritation and tugged at the collar of his shirt. "Vali seems to think she wants to talk with him . . . privately."

"Why?"

The man glanced nervously around the room, focusing on a small photograph of Vali Tremayne. "Apparently she's feeling the need for help," he replied, his tone caustic.

"What did the blind man tell her?"

"He agreed. I think she's planning on trying to see him sometime tomorrow."

"I knew we should have acted on my original instincts," the voice at the other end of the line snapped.

"*No!* My way is best. Just keep an eye on the Kaines—I'll take care of the rest of it."

The other man said nothing for a moment. When he finally

spoke again, his voice was oiled with a smirk. "You want her, don't you? You've fallen for her."

"I've never pretended to be indifferent to her."

"That's quite true, you haven't. Up to now, however, you've shown an admirable restraint of your feelings."

"My feelings are my business."

"Only if they don't interfere with the work."

"They never have, have they?"

"Not until recently." He paused. "All right. Continue as you have been, at least for now. We'll take care of the Kaines."

"Be careful. The man is no fool."

"Don't worry, we'll be discreet. Just get on with your part." After a petulant sigh, he added, "All these complications annoy me. You used to be such an easy man to work with. Lately you've become troublesome. *Do* try to be somewhat less tiring, won't you?"

The man hung up, scowling at the photograph beside him. It was true that he wasn't entirely mindless of Vali's appeal. Still, he had no intention whatsoever of allowing her to complicate his life any more than she already had. Like anyone else who got in the way of the work, she was expendable.

FOURTEEN

THE ferry from Catawba to Middle Bass Island wasn't crowded. It was a weekday, and the tourist season was over. Still, several people were aboard, enough to provide a steady hum of conversation.

"I think we're going to have another beautiful day," Jennifer said to Daniel, shading her eyes with one hand as she glanced up into the bright, cloudless sky.

They were sitting on metal benches on the outer deck. Jennifer had tied a bandanna over her hair to protect it from the spray off the lake. Dan held a large picnic basket on his lap.

"What's for lunch?" he asked, tapping the cover of the basket.

"All kinds of good stuff from that deli up the road. Fried chicken, potato salad, ham and cheese, rolls—oh, and a pound cake."

"Mmm. We'll have to take a doggie bag back to Sunny."

"Poor thing, she hasn't had much fun on this trip," Jennifer said, linking her arm through Dan's. "I wish now we had brought her along. But it would have been awkward, with the ferry and going biking and all."

Dan pulled his mouth into a skeptical line. "We're really going to do this, huh? The tandem bike, I mean."

"That's the best way to see the island, Daniel."

"I can't *see* the island, Jennifer," he reminded her dryly. "And you've already seen it. So why can't we just walk around for a while and then eat?"

"Biking is good exercise, Daniel. You were grumbling just yesterday about needing exercise." She patted her abdomen. "And so do I. You're not worried about riding a bike, are you?"

He grinned. "You're probably the one who should be worried, darlin'. Having me along may cramp your style just a little."

"Not a chance. It'll be fun. And romantic. There's something very romantic about a bicycle built for two."

"Jennifer, take my word for it. There is nothing even remotely romantic about a grown man taking a tumble into the bushes. Even if the woman he loves is tumbling right behind him."

"Daniel, any man who isn't afraid to ride the *Magnum* can't possibly be intimidated by a bicycle."

"Wanna bet?"

She elbowed him and turned to survey their fellow passengers. Directly across from them sat two young Asian men with cameras strapped around their necks. On the same row of seats were an elderly man and woman. The woman had little round wire-rimmed glasses perched on an upturned nose and was smiling at Jennifer wisely, as if she could tell she was a newlywed.

Jennifer returned the woman's smile, then let her gaze move farther up the deck. A middle-aged man with a briefcase was reading a science fiction paperback. A few seats away, three college-age girls were deep in conversation.

Had her attention not been caught by the flaming red hair of one of the girls, she probably would never have noticed the man standing close to them. Her admiring glance went from the fiery curls of the coed to the glistening bald dome of the man towering above her. He looked familiar somehow, and when he moved, Jennifer caught a better glimpse of his profile.

She gasped, staring at him with astonishment. *He looked like the man she had seen at Cedar Point!* Unexpectedly, he moved toward the corner of the deck and disappeared. Jennifer got up, her gaze scanning the deck. But the man was nowhere in sight.

"Jennifer?" Dan called in a puzzled voice.

Jennifer went back and sat down, immediately searching the passengers again for some glimpse of the burly, bald-headed stranger.

"Honey? Is something wrong?"

Hearing the troubled note in Daniel's voice, Jennifer took his hand, hurrying to reassure him. "No, nothing," she said. "I thought I saw someone I knew, but I was wrong."

Still, she continued to study the other passengers, half hoping she wouldn't see the man again, yet at the same time disturbed that she had seen him at all—and that he had managed to disappear so quickly.

✦

"Well—did you or didn't you enjoy the bicycle ride?" Jennifer asked smugly as she pitched their napkins and paper plates into a nearby trash receptacle.

Dan stood up, gave a huge stretch, and yawned. "It was an experience, I have to admit."

"Is this the first time you've been on a bike since the accident?"

He nodded. "Gabe has tried to talk me into it a couple of times, but I didn't take to the idea."

"But you do so many other things," she pointed out. "You told me you go horseback riding with the kids at the farm. And you bowl. And swim, of course."

"Speaking of swimming—"

"You've already spoken of swimming," Jennifer interrupted. "Several times, as a matter of fact. I'm beginning to think my competition is going to be a pool."

"You'll never have any competition, darlin'. But you know what they say—if you can't beat 'em . . ."

"So you can laugh me out of the pool again, like you did at Gatlinburg last week? No thanks."

"I didn't laugh at you," Dan insisted, a suspicious hint of a smile playing at the corners of his mouth.

"I told you before we got married that I can't swim like a fish," Jennifer said self-righteously.

"But you *didn't* tell me," he countered with a smirk, "that you still used an inner tube." When Jennifer made no reply, he added, "Don't worry about it. As soon as we get back to Shepherd Valley, you're going to have yourself some private lessons. You'll be Olympic material in no time."

Jennifer rolled her eyes skeptically. "I'll settle for learning how to negotiate a decent front crawl."

Walking around to her side of the picnic table, Dan caught her hand and kissed her lightly on the cheek. "Find me a tree, love."

"A tree?" Jennifer stared at him blankly, then caught on. "You're about to take a nap, right?"

"Ten minutes?"

"I'm wise to your ten-minute snoozes, Daniel. It's like trying to wake a grizzly in December."

Protesting all the way, she guided him to an enormous old cottonwood tree, where both of them dropped to the ground. Dan leaned against the trunk and wrapped his arms around Jennifer. She rested against the broad expanse of his chest, glancing around their surroundings with lazy contentment. The picnic area was a quiet, secluded little glen with warm sunshine trickling through the trees overhead. The air was tangy with the faint, damp smell of the lake. It was a special time and a special place, and at least for now, it belonged only to them.

"Are you happy, Jennifer?" Dan asked quietly, tightening his arms around her.

"Oh, Daniel—if I were any happier, I'd . . . I'd explode!"

He rested his chin on top of her head. "Have I thanked you today for marrying me?"

"Mm. I think so. Once or twice, anyway." Jennifer tipped her head to look up at him. His smile was soft and thoughtful. "What about you, Daniel? Are you happy?"

He pressed his lips to her temple. "Ah, love, . . . 'happy' isn't a big enough word for it." He paused. "You know, before the Lord brought you into my life, I used to wake up every morning after the accident, and for the first few minutes I literally had to *force* myself to face reality, to . . . *condition* my mind all over again to the darkness. Even after five years, it was still hard for me to put on the truth each morning and start all over."

He brushed a gentle kiss into her hair. "But now . . . now I wake up, and I lie there listening to you breathing so soft and easy beside me. I feel your warmth, and I think about our love . . . and I don't mind the darkness anymore. Now I wake up to sunshine every morning."

Jennifer's eyes misted with tears, and she lifted her face for his kiss. Then she sighed and pressed her face against his shoulder. "Oh, Daniel, let's always love each other like this. Let's never, ever let our love get old or stale or—predictable."

He smiled at the depth of emotion in her voice, and there was a light chuckle in his tone when he answered. "Darlin'," he murmured into her hair, "somehow, I find it hard to believe that anything about life with you—or our love—will ever be predictable."

He kissed her again, and Jennifer snuggled close. After several minutes of silence, she turned in his arms to look up at him. "Daniel, what do you think about Vali? Do you think she's right about there being something wrong with her mind?"

He shook his head. "No, I don't think so. Oh, there's something wrong," he added quickly. "But if you're asking me if I think Vali has serious mental problems, no, I don't."

He shook his head. "Every time I'm with Vali," he said thoughtfully, "I get the impression of someone who's extremely insecure, someone with very little self-esteem. David has confirmed my observation, by the way." His tone was gloomy as he went on. "As serious as that can be in itself, I'm not so sure it's the primary problem."

His expression grew even more grim, and Jennifer felt her own concern deepen. "What are you thinking, Daniel?"

"I wish I could see Vali's eyes," he replied slowly. "There's something . . . not quite right about her speech, but I can't put my finger on it. Haven't you noticed that at times her voice has virtually no inflection at all? It's almost as if she's not entirely aware of her own words. There's a certain flatness there that isn't typical. And the way she stumbles over her words. Doesn't that strike you as a little peculiar for a singer?"

Jennifer stared at him. He was right. She would never have realized it on her own, but Dan had just pinpointed one of the things she had found vaguely disconcerting about Vali from the beginning.

"What do you think it means, Daniel?"

"I can't be sure, but one of two things, I think. If only I could see her eyes," he said again, "I could be more certain. That lack of expression and nuance in her voice could indicate a specific emotional problem—I'm thinking of depression. Or she could be on some kind of mood-altering prescription."

Jennifer frowned. "You don't think Vali is taking drugs, do you?"

He shook his head. "Not in the sense you mean. But she could be under a physician's care and taking a prescription drug."

"But you don't think so." Jennifer saw the doubt in his expression. "Do you?"

He hesitated. "I don't think it's likely that Vali would have asked me for help if she were already seeing a doctor for her problems. Besides, Graham made it fairly clear that she isn't."

"Well, whatever it is," Jennifer said with assurance as she settled back into his embrace, "I know you'll be able to help her."

He rubbed his chin across the top of her head. "Don't be so sure, Jennifer. It's not likely I'll have time to even find out what the problem is, much less help her solve it. I only agreed to talk with her because I thought I might be able to convince her to see a doctor who *can* help."

They remained silent for a long time. Jennifer found herself wondering if either of the two men in Vali's life played a part in her emotional struggles, and if so, which one. Or could *both* Graham Alexander and David Nathan Keye somehow be responsible for the troubled young singer's problems?

After a few more minutes, she heard Dan's breathing grow even and shallow. She turned to look up at him, smiling when she saw that he was sound asleep. She kissed him lightly on the cheek, then burrowed more comfortably into his arms for a short nap of her own.

Half an hour later, the man with the field glasses saw them get up, tie their windbreakers around their waists, and stow their picnic supplies in the bicycle basket. After a quick look around the area, they got on the tandem bike, the blind man on the seat in back of the woman.

The man lowered the field glasses and sprinted to the car parked a few feet away. He cranked the powerful engine to life and pulled out onto the narrow road.

As soon as he had the bike in view, he slowed the car, staying at least a quarter of a mile behind.

He followed at that distance for a few minutes, continuously checking the rearview mirror. There was no one else on the road. He glanced from one side to the other and, seeing no pedestrians, applied a little more pressure to the accelerator, keeping the couple on the bike clearly in sight. Staring straight ahead, he lowered the gas pedal even more, then floored it. The car belched a loud roar and lunged forward, directly toward the tandem bike just ahead.

Jennifer heard the sound of the engine and glanced back over her shoulder to see what was happening. She panicked at the sight of the car closing in on them and uttered a choked cry of alarm. The bike swerved sharply to the left.

"Jennifer? What is it?" Dan put a steadying hand on her shoulder.

Facing forward, Jennifer tried to pedal faster, then turned to look behind them once more. "There's a car—coming straight at us!"

A wave of terror swept through her. The sedan was barreling down on them like an angry black tornado.

For a split second, Jennifer froze and almost lost control of the bike. Her hands began to shake on the handlebars. Her throat constricted with a rising knot of panic.

"Dan—*he's going to hit us!*"

Staring back in shocked disbelief, Jennifer didn't see the deep chuckhole in the road until the bike hit it full force. Stunned, she heard Dan cry out, felt him grab for her, heard the squeal of tires and her own shriek of terror as the bike flew off the road and crashed into a ditch.

The speeding sedan roared past them without slowing. Jennifer caught only a fleeting glimpse of the driver when he snapped his head around to look at them, lying helplessly in the ditch.

It was the same man she had seen at Cedar Point—the same man she thought she had seen on the ferry. The bald man with the eerie, pale eyes.

FIFTEEN

WHEN the phone rang late the next morning, Jennifer was in the bathroom applying ointment to the scratches on her face and arms. She hadn't exaggerated when she told Daniel she looked as if she'd been dragged across a gravel road.

Daniel had somehow emerged from the bicycle crash without a scratch, although he had wrenched his shoulder and bruised a rib or two. He had done his best to absorb most of the fall, holding on to Jennifer and trying to keep her on top as they were thrown into the ditch. But the impact had thrown her away from him at the last minute.

Once the shock wore off, they walked to the bike rental and called the police. The officer who talked with them was polite and concerned, but offered little hope for finding the man who had tried to run them down. Without a license number or specific description of the car, he explained, it would be difficult, if not impossible, to trace the driver.

Only after they returned to the cottage did Jennifer tell Dan that she was positive the driver of the car had been the same man who had aroused her suspicions at Cedar Point. She also confided that she was now fairly certain he had been on the ferry that morning.

Dan had finally admitted that he, too, was beginning to believe there might be a link between the events at the amusement park, the intruder at Vali's cottage, and the incident with the black sedan.

He had gone on to explain that he suspected someone of trying to terrorize Vali—or, worse, actually harm her.

Jennifer was still staring at herself in the mirror, thinking about his troubling suspicion, when Dan walked into the bathroom. "Jennifer, are you sure you shouldn't see a doctor?"

"No, really, I'm all right." She replaced the tube of ointment in her travel kit and turned to him. "Who was on the phone?"

"Vali. She wanted to know if she could come over—or if we would mind stopping by. I told her what happened and explained that you're not feeling too great. She's going to walk over here in a few minutes. Is that all right?"

"Yes, of course. But—"

"What?"

Jennifer sighed. "I'm beginning to feel really guilty about all this."

Dan closed the distance between them, taking her hand. "What are you talking about?"

"Daniel, it's all my fault that we got caught up in this. If I hadn't been so curious our first day up here, we probably wouldn't have people trying to run us down."

"That's a little irrational, even for you, sweetheart."

"Daniel—"

He made a gesture to stop her protest. "I mean it, Jennifer. In the first place, we don't know that what happened to us yesterday has anything to do with what's been going on with Vali."

"You think it does," Jennifer said stubbornly.

He put his hands on her shoulders. "Even so, you didn't go looking for trouble."

"Well, whether I went looking for it or not, I've certainly managed to foul up our honeymoon," Jennifer said miserably.

For a moment Dan stood unmoving, as if he were considering her words. Then a trace of a smile touched his lips. "I don't know about you, darlin'," he said softly, framing Jennifer's face between his hands, "but *I* think our honeymoon has been nothing short of wonderful."

Jennifer studied him. "Really, Daniel?"

"Absolutely," he whispered. With infinite tenderness, he scanned her face with his fingertips, a mannerism Jennifer had grown to love. Gently, he brushed a wave of hair away from her cheek. Then, still smiling the sweet, soft little smile that never failed to make her heart spin, he pressed a kiss on her forehead. Jennifer closed her eyes, and he kissed them, too. Then she smiled, and he kissed her lips. Thoroughly.

At last he lifted his face from hers with a little sound of regret.

"Then you're not feeling neglected?" Jennifer murmured.

He touched one finger to her mouth and shook his head. "A little crowded, maybe. Husbands are like that, you know."

"I'm afraid I don't know very much about husbands yet," Jennifer confessed softly into the warmth of his shoulder.

"Ah, you're doing fine, sweetheart," he told her, pressing one more kiss to her cheek. "You're doing just fine."

Dan could hear the strain and uncertainty in Vali's voice almost from the moment she arrived at the cottage. Jennifer, pleading the need to soak her soreness away in a hot tub, left them alone. Even then, Vali avoided her reason for coming. After a few minutes of idle pleasantries, Dan finally took the lead.

"I thought we might hear from you yesterday," he said. "When did you come back to the cottage?"

"Early this morning. The phone was in service again by yesterday morning, but it took longer to get the door fixed."

"I don't imagine it was easy, coming back after that incident with the prowler," Dan said carefully.

"It was awful. I felt . . ." She hesitated.

"Violated?" Dan prompted quietly.

"Yes—that's it exactly! It was as if somebody had intruded not only on my privacy, but on my *self*—my person—as well."

Dan nodded with understanding. "I'm sure you could have stayed with Leda for a few days. She's obviously very fond of you."

"Oh, Leda is wonderful," Vali said quickly. "And I love her as much as if she were my own mother." She stopped, then went on. "At least, I think I do. I never knew my mother."

Over the next few minutes, she explained to Dan that her natural parents had abandoned her when she was still a toddler and that she had grown up in foster homes until, at the age of fourteen, she was adopted by a Nashville policeman and his wife.

Dan knew Vali was still being evasive, but he had been prepared for that.

"Do you still see your adoptive parents?" he asked.

"Uncle Bill—that's what I called him—died just before I graduated from college," Vali explained. "Aunt Mary still lives in Nashville. We talk by phone at least once a week."

Dan leaned back in his chair and smiled. "Vali, what did you mean the other night at Leda's? When you told me you were afraid, but you're not sure what you're afraid of?"

He heard her deep intake of breath, as if she hadn't expected his directness.

"After everything that's happened lately, I'm beginning to think I have even more reason to be frightened than I knew then."

"But that isn't what you meant the other night, is it?" Dan asked gently.

"No," Vali admitted after a long hesitation. "It's just that sometimes—often—I feel afraid. Anxious. Almost . . . terrified." She faltered, then went on. "It's as if I'm expecting something to happen, something awful, something that I can't control. But I don't know what."

Dan frowned. "You say this happens often. How often, Vali?"

"Oh, I don't know . . . maybe once every couple of days. Yes," she said after a moment, "at least that."

"And you have no idea why?"

"No," she replied, sounding forlorn. "I've tried to remember, but—"

Dan interrupted. "Why do you say 'remember'?"

Vali didn't answer right away. When she finally spoke, Dan heard a note of surprise in her voice. "I just realized that whatever it is I dread so terribly . . . it's something that happened a long time ago. Something bad."

Dan was quiet for a long time, lightly rapping his fingers on the tabletop. "Do you remember when you first started to have these anxiety attacks, Vali?"

After a long pause, Vali answered, her voice low. "Yes, I remember. It was. . . ." She stopped, then abruptly asked, "You know about Paul's death—the plane crash?"

Dan nodded.

"After Paul died, I had—they *said* I had—a breakdown. I was in a hospital for months. . . . I don't remember exactly how long."

Dan suddenly became aware of the gradual change in her voice. She was dropping back into the flat, expressionless tone he had heard before. The longer she talked, he noticed, the more pronounced the monotone became.

"After I was well enough to leave the hospital, I stayed with Leda for a few weeks. Then I bought my cottage here at the lake."

"But when did you start feeling so . . . afraid?" Dan prompted gently.

"Afraid?" There was a long silence. When Vali finally spoke, her voice had cleared and sounded stronger. "It was while I was still at Leda's, I think. Yes," she said with more assurance, "it started then. I remember, because I had to start taking the medicine again."

"Medicine?" Dan sat forward. "What medicine was that?"

"Let's see, what did Graham call it? I don't remember. Some kind of tranquilizer he got from Dr. Devries at the hospital."

"Your doctor prescribed it?"

"I suppose so. He gave Graham some samples the day I left the hospital. Once Graham found out what the medication was, he got a generic brand of the same thing from one of the doctors at the Center."

"The Center?"

"Graham's laboratory."

"They have medical doctors there, too?"

"Oh, yes. Graham says that more than half of the research people are medical doctors. They even have psychiatrists and psychologists."

"I see." Something flashed briefly in Dan's mind, then fled. "What exactly does Graham do, Vali? What kind of research is he in?"

"Oh, Daniel," she said, laughing a little at herself, "I'm afraid I don't understand it well enough to begin to explain. It's all very technical. Graham is primarily a chemist, I believe. He's the director of research at the Center. They do a number of different things, mostly with pharmaceutical research and development, I think."

Dan nodded slowly. "This medicine, Vali—Graham gets it for you?"

"That's right. I've tried to pay for it any number of times, but he won't let me. He says they get tons of samples at the Center and I might as well use some of it. I really don't like taking things from him—he and Leda have already done so much for me—but he refuses to let me pay."

"I understand." Dan *didn't* understand, not really, and his doubts about Graham Alexander were increasing by the minute. "Graham is very fond of you, isn't he?"

"Yes," Vali said, her voice even softer. "He wants to marry me. In fact . . ."

Her voice drifted off, and Dan prompted her again. "What, Vali?"

"He . . . bought me a ring. Last night he took me to dinner, and he had the ring with him."

Dan lifted his brows. "Are you wearing it now?"

"No," she said quietly. "Not . . . yet."

"Do you mind my asking why?" Dan said carefully.

"No . . . I don't mind. It's just that I'm . . . very confused about my feelings for Graham."

Dan waited, saying nothing.

"I still . . . can't seem to forget about Paul," she added, her voice strained.

"I don't think anyone would expect you to forget him," Dan said. "You loved Paul Alexander a great deal, didn't you, Vali?" he asked softly.

"He was my life," she said, her voice surprisingly strong.

Dan nodded, feeling a wave of compassion for her. "I'm sure Paul would want you to be happy, to love again, after all this time."

"I *want* to!" Her harsh outburst startled Dan. "I *want* to love Graham. He looks after me. He's wonderfully good to me. . . . I *owe* it to him to love him."

Dan measured his words with great care. "Vali, you can't use love to pay a debt."

He heard her voice falter. "I know . . . it's just that I want *so much* to love Graham. Sometimes I wish David had never come up here. I—"

"David?" Dan frowned and rubbed his hand over his chin. "So David is complicating things for you?"

For a moment he wondered if he had said too much. But she

finally answered, her tone halting and uncertain. "David . . . cares for me, too." She paused, then added, "At least, he says he does."

"And that disturbs you?"

"David is a . . . disturbing man." She paused. "Sometimes . . . sometimes he reminds me of Paul."

"Do you think that's why you're attracted to him?"

"I'm not!" She stopped, and Dan said nothing, waiting.

"That's not true. I *am*. But not because he reminds me of Paul. The very things I felt drawn to in Paul seem to . . . to intimidate me in David." She laughed weakly. "That doesn't make sense, does it?"

Dan shrugged. "Our feelings often don't make sense, I'm afraid."

"I'm not sure what I feel for David," Vali admitted. "I enjoy being with him—he makes me feel . . . good about myself. Paul could always do that, too."

Daniel heard the slight tremor in her voice as she went on. "But sometimes David almost . . . frightens me. It's as if there's something I ought to know about him, something important, but—" She broke off, then choked out a rush of words, her frustration unmistakable. "Oh, I don't know! I just don't *know!*"

Dan could hear the growing strain in her voice. The storm of emotions he had sensed in Vali over the last hour troubled him. The young woman sitting across from him was so complex, her emotional state so fragmented, that it was difficult to sort out what he had heard with any degree of objectivity.

As honestly—and as gently—as possible, he explained to her his own need to think about some of the things she had told him. "And there's something I want you to be thinking about, too, Vali," he said. "What you said, about Paul—and David—making you feel good about yourself, making you feel special . . . that's important, having people in your life who care about you and make you feel that you matter to them, that you're special. But it's absolutely vital that you realize you *are* special, no matter what anyone else may think."

"I'm sorry," she said, "I don't understand."

"Vali, you can't—and you don't have to—base your identity on what another person thinks about you." Dan leaned forward, intent on making her understand. "You *are* special, Vali—very special—because you're a child of God. Because God made you. Because he saved you. Because he loves you. It's your relationship with *God* that makes you what you are, who you are—and enables you to be everything you can be."

He tapped his fingers on the table, thinking. "Let me give you just a couple of things to consider and pray about, OK? If you have any question about what you are in the eyes of the Lord, read Psalm 139: 'For you created my inmost being; you knit me together in my mother's womb. I praise you because I am fearfully and wonderfully made; your works are wonderful, I know that full well.'

Dan went on, smiling. "One of my personal favorites is 1 John 3:1: 'How great is the love the Father has lavished on us, that we should be called children of God! And that is what we are!'"

He thought for a minute, then added, "Remember this, Vali. You count . . . you matter. If you weren't important to another soul in the world, you would still be someone very special. Not so much because you're *you*—but more because you're *his*."

Vali was silent for a long time. Finally she said, very simply, "Daniel . . . I'm not sure, but I think you may have just given me a very precious gift."

Dan sensed the unshed tears in her voice, but there was something else he was resolved to bring up before she left. "Vali, one more thing. I'm a little concerned about this medication you're taking. You don't really know what it is, and—"

Instantly defensive, she stopped him. "Graham wouldn't give me anything harmful, Daniel!"

Dan made a dismissing gesture with one hand. "I'm not suggesting he would. I'm sure Graham wants only to help. But apparently you've been taking it for quite some time without knowing what it is."

Dan took a deep breath and phrased his words carefully. "Vali, under normal circumstances I wouldn't suggest this, but it seems that there might be a connection between this medication and your anxiety attacks. If your personal physician had prescribed the medicine, I'd say you should talk to him about it. But—" He paused, groping for words. "I'd be interested in seeing what happens if you don't take the medication . . . if you wean yourself off of it gradually."

With a sigh, Dan shifted and listened for Vali's response. If he was right—and he was pretty sure he was—that unknown medication could account for a lot of Vali's problems.

"Vali?" he prompted after a moment. "What do you think?"

Vali's reply was slow in coming. "I suppose . . . if you don't think it would hurt me. But I only take one pill every other day, Daniel."

Dan thought that was a peculiar dosage. "When do you take it? What time of day?"

"Just before I go to bed."

"Did you have one last night?"

"No."

"So you'd be due to take a pill tonight?"

"That's right."

"How about skipping tonight's dosage? To see how you feel tomorrow?"

"Well . . . I suppose that would be all right."

Dan stood up. "If you start feeling bad, let me know right away. Or if you have any side effects at all, we'll get in touch with a doctor. But try to go through tonight and tomorrow without it, why don't you?"

"All right. But I doubt that I'll notice any difference, Daniel. Graham said it's very mild."

Dan heard her get up. "I really should be getting back to the cottage now. David will be coming by soon to rehearse."

"How's it going?" Dan said, matching her abrupt change in mood with a cheerful tone of voice. "Have you made any decision yet about your career?"

He could hear the uncertainty in her reply. "David's music makes it awfully tempting. To tell you the truth, this is the first time since . . . since Paul died that I've begun to feel a desire—a need—to sing again. But . . ."

When she didn't finish her thought, Dan completed it for her. "You don't know if you can handle it—emotionally?"

She sighed. "That's right." After a slight hesitation, she added, "And Graham doesn't want me to go back. He wants us to be married soon and live up here."

Dan walked her to the door, with Sunny following. "Well, speaking as a radio man, I'm going to be hoping for a new album from you soon. And speaking as a friend," he added, "I feel exactly the same way. I can't help but believe that a gift like yours is meant to be shared."

"Thanks, Daniel. And thank you for talking with me. Tell Jennifer good-bye for me."

After Vali had gone, Dan returned to the table and sat down. He was vaguely aware of Jennifer singing in the bathroom; then he heard her turn on the blow-dryer.

He raked a hand through his hair and sighed. Out of the entire conversation with Vali, two things bothered him most. One was her comment about sometimes feeling afraid of David, and the other was the discovery that she had been taking medication for years without a doctor's supervision. What especially troubled him about the latter was Graham Alexander's involvement. If the man cared as much for Vali as he pretended, wouldn't he be more conscientious about giving her lab samples for medication?

Dan admitted to himself that he was just as put off by the scientist as Jennifer seemed to be. It bothered him, however, that he and Jennifer were apparently at odds in their feelings about David Nathan Keye. Jennifer had had conflicting feelings toward David from the beginning, whereas Dan instinctively trusted the man. Still, he couldn't gauge Keye's facial expressions or body language as Jennifer could, so he tended to be cautious about trusting David too much. The truth was, however, that he had been silently cheering the composer on in the contest for Vali's affection.

This was one of the times he felt more keenly than usual the restrictive nature of his disability. Although he knew the Lord had given him a certain amount of discernment, he never felt wholly secure in his sightless perceptions of others.

Except, of course, for his perception of his wife, who suddenly interrupted his reverie by sliding onto his lap, the sweet sunshine fragrance of her hair falling across his face as she planted a kiss on his cheek.

His vision of Jennifer was altogether different. God had placed a picture of her in his heart—a picture painted with divine perfection and the unerring accuracy of love.

SIXTEEN

V ALI awoke in a panic, bolting upright in bed, gasping for breath, her heart pounding wildly.

She had dreamed of Paul. But not Paul the way
she remembered him. His face had been angry, thunderous; his
mouth set in a thin, hard line; his eyes scalding with rage and dark
with warning.

The digital clock beside the bed registered 3:00 A.M. With a
sigh, she sank back onto the pillows and for a few minutes tossed
restlessly, still unsettled. When she finally fell asleep again, it was
only to have the dreams resume. Frame after frame of terrible
images assaulted her—pictures of the plane crash in which Paul
had been killed, pictures she remembered from the newspapers
and those she had only imagined during the long, tortured nights
at the hospital. Flashes of fire, the plane ablaze, everything burned.
Paul inside the inferno.

*No remains . . . everything burned . . . nothing but ashes . . . no
remains . . .*

This time when she woke up she was ill, her stomach pitching,
her throat hot and swollen. Her hands trembled with fear as she
clutched the sheet around her shoulders.

Four-thirty. Too troubled to sleep, Vali got up, went to the
kitchen, and poured a glass of juice. She drank it fast. Too fast. Her
stomach rebelled, and she ran for the bathroom.

Finally exhausted, her entire body covered with a film of

115

clammy perspiration, she went back to bed, pulled the sheet and the spread over her, and once again fell into an uneasy sleep.

This time she dreamed of the man at the Ferris wheel and the macabre carousel ride, then of Graham and Paul. Paul was staring at her with disappointment, as if she had failed him in some way. *"Betrayal . . . ,"* he said slowly, his eyes burning into hers. Over and over he repeated that one word. *"Betrayal . . ."*

At seven-thirty, she got up, feeling as if she had never been in bed. Her head throbbed, her eyes were grainy and irritated, and her stomach was in spasms. She tried to eat some dry toast but threw most of it away.

After making her bed and doing a load of laundry, she made a halfhearted attempt to do some breathing exercises and scale warm-ups. Within a few minutes, however, she gave up. She was tired—incredibly tired. With a sigh, she lay down on the bed and covered her eyes with her hand.

Her head was assaulted by a mind-squeezing pressure. A crashing wave of pain was followed by a brief, heavily veiled image of a bald-headed man walking toward her. His pale, icy stare loomed at her out of a mist. Someone was beside him . . . a tall man . . . a man with no face.

Vali lay there for an hour, trying to rest, but tormented by the images that would not go away. At last she got up and went to the kitchen. She needed busywork, something to occupy her hands, something that required little cooperation from her mind. Her eyes fell on a pathetic, pot-bound African violet, and she focused on transplanting it with all her energy.

The window above the sink was open, and she could hear the sound of whitecaps slapping rhythmically at the shore. The lake was choppy, the air close. She rinsed her hands, reached for a paper towel—and nearly slammed her head against the cabinet as another unexpected bolt of hot pain sent her groping for a chair.

Quickly, she put her head down, framing her face between her hands. A white blaze of light hurtled forward in her mind and froze like a halo around Paul's face. He was wearing the crewneck sweater and corduroy jeans he had been wearing the last time Vali had seen him. He had come to tell her about the unexpected trip, to say good-bye, to tell her . . .

She waited for her memory of Paul to end there, as it always did. He would walk into her living room in the townhouse in Nashville wearing the funny, crooked little smile he always wore when he looked at her. He would drop his hands gently to her shoulders, murmur, *"Angel"*—his private endearment for her— then disappear. Out of her vision, out of her life.

From that point on, she would remember nothing until the memorial service. She would see herself, sitting at the front of the church. . . . She would hear the organ sounding one of Paul's own praise anthems. . . . She would be aware of quiet weeping, subdued whispers, the chokingly sweet, heavy scent of flowers . . . Leda beside her, clutching her hand, looking strong and heartbroken at the same time . . . Graham on the other side of her, his taut features carved in restrained mourning.

Always, there was that gap in her memory, like a deep, silent chasm separating those last few moments with Paul from the memorial service. Until now. Now a misty vignette began to inch its way into her mind. Once more she saw Paul's smile, heard him whisper, "Angel."

But this time there was more. The vision was shattered, like pieces spilling out of a bottle. Paul gripped her forearms, his face lined with worry. *"If anything happens to me, don't trust anyone but my mother. Do you understand me, Angel? She's the only one you can trust."*

Startled, Vali sat upright. What did it mean? What had Paul been trying to tell her?

Chilled and still trembling, Vali got up from the chair and

began to pace the room. This was the first time since the plane crash that a new thread of memory had appeared. Why now?

A sudden thought struck her, and she stopped walking. *The medicine!*

She had skipped last night's pill, as Daniel Kaine had suggested. She thought it unlikely that the missing dosage could be responsible for the headaches, the baffling dreams, the bursts of memory. But over the next two hours, the flashes of memory repeated themselves. Each grew more intense, more troubling.

By noon, Vali was frightened to the point of panic and decided to call Daniel. She was surprised at how quickly he responded to her question about the medication.

"No, I definitely don't think it's coincidence, Vali," he told her. "I think we need to find out as much as we can about the pills you've been taking and whatever it is that's trying to fight its way out of your subconscious."

"But, Daniel—Graham wouldn't give me anything that would hurt me! And I have no idea what these . . . memory flashes are."

Dan was quiet for a moment. "Do you think Leda could be of any help?" he finally asked. "That statement of Paul's you mentioned—about not trusting anyone but his mother—maybe Leda would be able to shed some light on that."

"I can't imagine how . . ."

"Vali, I think we should talk with Leda," Dan said firmly.

"I suppose . . . if you really think it's important, I could call Leda and see if she'd mind our driving in later today. It would have to be after four, though. She writes from early morning until three-thirty or four every day."

"Fine. Listen, why don't Jennifer and I come over so you won't be alone?"

"Oh . . . no. I'm all right. But, Daniel—do you think Jennifer would drive, if we go to Leda's? I don't think I'd be very safe behind the wheel today."

"I'm sure she'll be glad to. We'll be there around four unless I hear from you, all right?"

When an insistent knock sounded at the door a few minutes later, Vali nearly jumped out of her skin. She opened the door to find David standing there.

"We were to rehearse at one-thirty, remember?"

"Oh, David—I forgot! I'm sorry, I should have called you. I can't possibly sing today."

He walked in without waiting to be asked. "What's wrong, Princess? Are you ill? You look awful."

Vali avoided his gaze, about to turn away from him, when he caught her arm. "Vali? What is it?"

"I'm . . . not feeling well," she said evasively. "I hope you don't mind if we cancel today."

"Can I do anything? Do you want me to call Leda?"

She shook her head. "No—I'll be all right. It's just . . . a bad headache."

Gently, he put a hand to her cheek. "You're sure that's all?"

Vali finally looked at him, her breath catching in her throat when she saw the tenderness in his eyes.

"Vali . . . Princess, what is it? What's wrong?"

Vali jumped when the phone rang, hesitating before crossing the room to answer.

Graham's warm, confident voice helped to steady her. "Are you all right, dear? You sound . . . peculiar."

"I'm fine . . . fine," Vali assured him. "I've had a headache most of the day, that's all."

"Probably your nerves," he said quickly. "Vali, I've been doing some thinking about this business of talking with Daniel Kaine. I really don't think it's wise. I spoke with a friend of mine earlier today. A psychologist, with an M.D. as well—very well respected in his field. If you really think you need counseling, he'll be glad to take you as a patient."

Vali drew in a long breath. "I . . . Graham . . . I've already talked with Daniel."

Instantly, his voice turned cold. "Wasn't that rather impetuous?"

"I—" She glanced at David, unnerved by the way he was studying her.

She heard Graham's deep sigh and knew he was groping for patience. *"And?"* he asked sharply.

Vali hesitated, reluctant to anger him. Still, he *was* responsible for giving her the medicine.

He was furious when she told him about the pills. "What an *incredibly* irresponsible suggestion for Kaine to make!" he exploded. "And you actually *listened* to him?"

"Graham, please . . . I have to do *something*. Don't you see that? I can't go on like this."

"What does that mean?"

"You know what it means." Vali felt an uncommon stab of irritation with him. *"You're* the one who's always reminding me of how fragile my emotions are."

There was a long silence. "I thought you trusted me," he finally said.

"I *do* trust you, Graham! But I can't go on living my life dependent upon you and your mother to make my decisions for me. Can't you understand?"

Graham's tone softened slightly. "Vali, I do understand. But you must be patient with yourself. And," he said pointedly, "you have to use good judgment. Now then—tell me exactly what Kaine suggested and how you've been feeling since."

He said little as Vali told him about her talk with Daniel. Occasionally he muttered a short sound of agreement or disagreement. But at least he no longer sounded angry.

"Vali, as mild as that medication is—and I can assure you that it *is* mild—you can't simply drop it all at once. Not without suffering at least some nominal side effects. And if Kaine were as qualified as he's led you to believe, he would have warned you of the possible consequences of missing even one of the pills."

"Graham, Daniel didn't try to mislead me. If anything, he was reluctant to even talk with me; he—"

"Yes, yes—I'm sure," he interrupted brusquely. "However, the point is that he had no business giving you advice at all." He paused. "So the headaches and these—*dreams* started last night."

"Yes."

"And you think they may be related to the pill you *didn't* take." He made no attempt to hide his sarcasm.

"I . . . I don't know what to think." Vali hesitated. "I thought perhaps if I talked with your mother—"

Graham didn't let her finish. "What in the world does *Mother* have to do with any of this?" he burst out.

Vali bit her lip, hesitating. "Daniel thought Leda might be able to help. Graham," she said carefully, "are you positive you can't remember anything at all about the last time you . . . were with Paul? You said the two of you talked. . . ."

"Vali," he said after a long silence, "I've already told you— several times—all there is to tell about that night. Paul came to the Center. We had coffee, talked for a few minutes, about you, mostly, and then he left."

Vali heaved a sigh of disappointment but said nothing. The weariness she had felt earlier now settled over her anew.

"I'll drive you in to Mother's later," Graham was saying, his tone now less annoyed. "I think I should be there, the way you've been feeling today."

He was so protective of her.

Too protective, something whispered at the back of her mind.

Vali shook off the thought. There really was something wrong with her if she could resent Graham's unflagging devotion to her, his thoughtfulness and consideration of her needs.

"I'd like you to be there, Graham. I was going to ask Jennifer to drive me, since I'm so shaky. But if you really want to . . ."

"I insist," he said firmly. "It will give me a chance to see you, after all." Sounding somewhat mollified, he told her good-bye and hung up.

Vali delayed turning back to David. When she did, she found him slouched against the piano, studying her with a searching stare.

"What kind of pills has Graham been giving you, Vali?" he asked harshly.

Vali had suddenly had enough. Her nerves were raw, her head was hammering, and she simply couldn't face another long explanation. "Since you obviously overheard our conversation, David, you shouldn't need any details," she snapped.

Something flared in his eyes—anger, she thought—but it quickly disappeared. Slowly he pushed himself away from the piano and walked over to her, his gaze never leaving her face. "I'm sorry. I suppose I shouldn't have listened. But you're right— I did hear the conversation. That's why I'm worried, Princess."

When Vali saw the soft warmth in his eyes, she regretted her sharpness. "David, I didn't mean to snap at you. It's this headache . . . and I didn't sleep. I must be more on edge than I realized."

"Vali." Gently, he put his hand on her shoulder. *"Do* you trust Graham? Do you really trust him?"

"Of course I trust Graham!"

David searched her gaze. "Are you in love with him?" he asked directly.

Surprised, Vali stammered, "I . . . you know I care for Graham. . . ."

"I asked if you're in love with him."

"You have no right, David. . . ."

"You still haven't answered me, Vali."

"I don't think that's any of your business."

Vali saw him swallow hard—once, then again. As she watched,

his expression gentled and his mouth softened to a sad, uncertain smile. "You're right. It's not."

Vali felt an unexpected sting of shame. "David . . ."

Slowly he lifted one hand, lightly grazed her cheek with his fingertips, then touched her hair. "I just want to see you happy, Princess," he whispered, his eyes caressing her face. "You're so special, Vali . . . so very, very special."

Vali felt tears scald her eyes, and she tried to turn away. But David caught her by the shoulders, turning her gently around to face him. Vali's heart stopped when she saw the look on his face. He was smiling at her, not a happy smile, but a wistful smile of regret that made her heart ache. For some inexplicable reason, she suddenly felt the need to comfort him.

"David . . ."

She stopped breathing as he bent his head to touch a featherlight kiss to her forehead. For one brief, tender moment, he circled her with his arms and gathered her carefully to him. Vali didn't know what to do, what to say. Awkwardly, she put her hands on his shoulders and stared up into his face.

"I'll go now, Princess," he whispered. "Try to get some rest, won't you? And forgive me if I upset you. Please?"

Vali nodded weakly as David slowly released her from his embrace and turned to go. She stood in silence, watching him leave, the tears fighting to spill over. She didn't understand the sweetness of emotion she had felt in his arms, nor the overwhelming sorrow she now felt in his absence.

But he had left something behind, something she knew she would cling to, just as she had savored the hope Daniel Kaine had given her yesterday. Dan had told her she was "special . . . not so much because you're *you*—but because you're *his* . . . because you're a child of God."

David, too, said she was "special . . . so very, very special."

She wanted—she *needed*—to believe them both.

SEVENTEEN

THE man answered the telephone reluctantly, muttering a grudging hello.

"So—did she talk to the blind man?" the voice at the other end of the line asked without preamble.

He hesitated, but not for long. "She talked to Kaine, yes."

"And?"

Again he paused before replying. "He . . . suggested that she skip the medication for a couple of days. To see how she would feel."

"And did she?"

He sighed. "Yes."

"With what consequences?"

"If the block isn't reinforced every forty-eight hours, control begins to fragment. At that point, it's quite possible for partial memory to break through."

"Am I to assume that this . . . breakthrough . . . has begun?"

He cleared his throat and mumbled a short, "Yes."

"Is there any possibility of getting her back on the medication immediately?"

"Not likely," the man grated. "I think Kaine has made her suspicious of the pills. She'll probably resist taking any more, at least for now."

"I see. So, my friend . . . are you ready to put an end to this business yet?"

He had anticipated the question, indeed had already reviewed his choices. They were few and impractical. "Yes. Let's get it over with."

"Ah . . . finally, an objective attitude." The caller paused. "Do you know where she will be tonight?"

"She and the Kaines are going to Sandusky," the man replied thinly. "They're looking for additional clues."

The caller laughed shortly. "Fine. We'll provide them with a few they aren't expecting. Kaine and his wife are both going?"

"I think so."

"Good. This will be easier than we thought. We can take care of all of them at the same time. Now—it would be wise for you to absent yourself from them for the entire evening. Also, we'll need to be certain the singer drives her own car."

"She's not planning on driving at all. She was going to ask the Kaine woman . . ."

"That's no problem. We'll simply render the Kaines' automobile useless, at least for the evening."

"What are you planning to do?"

"You needn't concern yourself with that. Just rest assured that everything will be handled quietly and neatly. After tonight, there will be no more loose ends."

"But shouldn't I be there? To make sure everything goes according to plan?"

"Not unless you want to die with the rest of them, my friend."

EIGHTEEN

JENNIFER, are you sure you don't mind driving?" Vali asked from the backseat. "Graham intended to take us until he got that phone call from Ohio State," she explained, adjusting her seat belt. "It turned out that he and David were both busy tonight."

"I don't mind a bit." Jennifer glanced in the rearview mirror as she pulled out onto Cleveland Road. "Just so long as you don't care if Sunny rides in your car."

Vali reached over to pet the retriever, who was perched on the seat beside her, staring out the window. "Sunny can go anywhere with me," she said, smiling. "Did you call the garage about your tire?"

Jennifer nodded. "I don't know where we picked up that nail, but I sure didn't want to drive all the way to Sandusky on that little doughnut they call a spare."

"Did they say when you can pick up your car?"

"Later this evening. I asked the mechanic to go ahead and change the oil and do a couple of other things while he was at it."

"I told you I'd do that when we get home." Dan, seated beside her, shook his head. "You're just wasting money."

Jennifer rolled her eyes at Vali in the mirror. "I thought I'd save you the trouble this time, Daniel."

"I *can* change the oil, Jennifer," he said somewhat testily.

"I know that."

"I change the oil in the station's Cherokee all the time."

She glanced at Vali again, lifting her eyebrows and grinning. "That's right, you do."

"How much is he charging you?"

"How much?" She looked at him.

"You didn't even ask?" Dan's expression was incredulous.

"Well . . . no, not exactly. I forgot."

Dan sighed.

"Next time I'll remember," Jennifer added meekly.

"Are you sure this guy even knows *how* to fix a tire?"

"All he has to do is remove the nail and patch the hole. He may not be Mr. Goodwrench, but I think he can handle it."

"Mm."

"Daniel . . ."

"Hm?"

"Are we having our first argument?"

"We had our first argument not long after we met, Jennifer."

"Good. I wouldn't want to have our first one in front of Vali."

After a second, Dan grinned. "Was I making noises like a husband?"

"That's what it sounded like."

"I'm just practicing."

"Well, you can quit. You got it right the first time."

"Turn your windshield wipers on, Jennifer."

She looked at him again. "How did you know it was drizzling?"

He shrugged. "The way the tires sound on the highway."

Jennifer muttered to herself but turned on the wipers.

"This road gets a little slippery when it's wet, Jennifer," Vali warned from the backseat.

"Don't worry, I'll be careful."

They drove along in silence for several minutes. Jennifer glanced in the rearview mirror every now and then, both for traf-

fic and to watch Vali. She could tell by the way the singer was act-
ing that she was still having "memory flashes," as Dan had called
them. And she was massaging her temples. The headache must still
be there, too.

Jennifer had a mild headache of her own, but she knew hers
was weather related. It had been warm and humid all day, and the
air was now close enough to be uncomfortable. She fiddled with
the air conditioning control, turning it up a notch.

"We're going to have a storm later," Dan said, breaking the
silence.

"Daniel has radar," Jennifer explained to Vali soberly.

"It's going to storm," he repeated with confidence.

"It probably will," his wife agreed grudgingly.

There was little traffic. Jennifer reached over to turn on the
radio, keeping the volume soft so it wouldn't aggravate Vali's—or
her own—headache. She played with the dial, eventually finding a
weather report.

*"Remember that a severe thunderstorm watch means conditions are
favorable for heavy thunderstorms. These storms may include dangerous
lightning and strong winds."*

"See," Daniel said smugly, "his radar picked up a storm, too."

Jennifer groaned and switched off the radio, focusing her attention on the road as the rain started to come down more heavily.
The two-lane highway to Sandusky was fairly flat, unlike the
roads back in West Virginia. But the rain was making the surface
slippery. As they headed into a curve, she felt the wheels slide, and
she gently tapped the brake.

"Take it easy, honey," Daniel cautioned.

"Sorry." Jennifer didn't dare hit the brakes any harder. She
gripped the wheel, relieved to feel the car settling into the curve.

As she came out of the turn, she glanced into the rearview mirror. Vali was sitting with her eyes tightly closed.

"Are you all right, Vali?" she began, then gasped as she saw a dark sedan careening up behind them at too high a speed to be safe on slippery roads.

Jennifer pushed on the accelerator, and Vali's Sentra lunged forward.

"What's wrong, Jennifer?" Daniel asked. "Why are you driving so fast?"

"Some idiot behind me is tailgating," Jennifer grated out, her eyes darting to the rearview mirror.

"Well, let him pass."

Jennifer let up on the gas, but the black sedan didn't go around her. Instead, it drew even closer, bearing down on them at an alarming speed. Panicked, Jennifer scanned the road ahead. A long curve to the right was coming up, a place where the car couldn't possibly pass unless the driver wanted to take the risk of a head-on collision with a vehicle on the blind curve.

Again she glanced in the mirror. The sedan was almost on her bumper now, and through the rain-glazed rear window she couldn't see the driver's face—only his bald head, bent low over the steering wheel, one hand holding a cellular telephone to his ear.

Jennifer's heart leaped into her throat. Instinctively she hit the brakes, intending to slide off onto the right-hand berm. Nothing happened. The black car lurched forward, slamming into the rear bumper of Vali's car, then began to accelerate, pushing them ahead, faster. Again Jennifer tried to apply the brakes. Her foot went all the way to the floorboard, with no result.

"We've lost the brakes!" she shouted, gripping the wheel until her knuckles went white. As if from a great distance, she could hear Daniel's voice, barking instructions to her, trying to help. Still the sedan pushed them forward, ever faster.

Jennifer hung on, praying frantically as she guided the car around the curve. The black sedan was still behind them, pushing them forward. Suddenly, on the other side of the curve, a huge panel truck appeared out of nowhere, blocking the highway.

"Hold on!" she screamed. With a final prayer, she wrenched the steering wheel sharply to the left. On two wheels the Sentra crossed the oncoming traffic lane and landed with a bone-jarring *thud* on the access ramp on the other side. Jennifer fought for control, narrowly missing a small green pickup truck coming down the ramp onto the highway.

When the incline of the ramp finally brought them to a stop, Jennifer threw the emergency brake, leaned over the wheel, and began to shake. No one said a word. Sunny whimpered once, and Daniel turned to give her a reassuring pat. Through the rear window, Jennifer could see the black sedan still sitting in the middle of the highway, its rear end fishtailed into the panel truck. The bald driver was nowhere in sight.

With a shuddering sigh, her hands locked on the steering wheel, she fought back the tears clouding her vision. Her chest felt as if someone had strapped a boulder on it. Her stomach began to riot, and her head felt about to explode.

After a few seconds, Dan drew in a long, shaky breath. "Jennifer? Are you all right?" His voice was thick and unsteady.

Jennifer had to wait until her teeth stopped chattering to answer him. "Y-yes," she said, still clutching the steering wheel.

"Vali?" Dan asked.

"I—yes. I'm . . . all right."

Dan reached over to touch Jennifer's hands. Very gently he pried one finger at a time from the wheel. "You did real good, love," he said softly. "That was quite a landing."

Finally able to move, Jennifer looked over at him. "There were no brakes," she said in a dazed voice. "Nothing."

Nodding, he squeezed her hand. "I know. But we're all right now; we're fine."

"I . . . couldn't stop . . . I couldn't . . . pull over . . . I . . ."

Quickly, Daniel released his seat belt and drew her to him. "Easy . . . easy. It's all right," he murmured, lightly stroking her back.

"It was the same man," Jennifer said in a low, tight voice against his shoulder. "He tried to kill us."

"What?"

"Vali, . . . did you see?" asked Jennifer. "The black car?"

"Yes," Vali said in a low, tremulous voice. "I saw it."

Daniel started to say something, but Jennifer stopped him. "It was *him,* Daniel. It was the man I saw at Cedar Point—the same man who ran our bicycle off the road. He . . . he's trying to kill us, Daniel!" She stopped and caught her breath. "Who *is* he?" Her cry was muffled against his chest.

"I don't know, honey. But what we have to do now is get some help. We can't drive without brakes."

Holding her with one arm, he pulled a handkerchief out of his back pocket.

"Is this white?" He held out the handkerchief for her inspection.

Jennifer stared at it for a moment, then looked blankly at Dan. "White?"

"For a signal," he explained.

"Oh—yes. Yes, it's white."

"Tie it to the antenna and raise the hood," he told her as the rain pattered softly on the car. "We'll just have to wait here until someone stops to help."

Within half an hour, a deputy sheriff arrived. After a few questions, he radioed for a wrecker to pick up the car, then drove all of them back to Vali's cottage.

It was nearly nine o'clock that night before Dan could get any information from the garage in Huron where Vali's car had been taken. Jennifer and Vali sat waiting on the sofa as he hung up the phone and turned toward them.

"The brake lines were cut," he said tersely.

"Cut?" Vali repeated in a shaky voice. "You mean someone deliberately . . ."

"That's right. Someone deliberately took out the brakes."

The room was thick with tension for several minutes. Vali finally broke the silence. "There's something I probably should have told you before now. But at the time, I didn't think it was important."

She told them about seeing the bald-headed man at the Ferris wheel at Cedar Point—the same man who had been driving the black sedan today.

"So you saw him at the Ferris wheel, before it broke down," Dan said thoughtfully. "And Jennifer saw him again at the carousel before . . ." He let the rest of the sentence drift off, unfinished.

He remained quiet for a long time. When he finally spoke, his voice was grave, his face as sober as Jennifer had ever seen it. "I think we need to consider something. I don't believe it's just coincidence that our car was put out of commission and Vali's brakes were tampered with anymore than it's coincidence that this guy—whoever he is—keeps showing up every time something weird happens."

When neither of the women said anything, he lightly rapped his knuckles against the countertop where he was standing, then went on. "It seems to me that someone wanted to make sure we drove Vali's car tonight instead of Jennifer's. And I'm afraid we can all figure out why."

He moved to the cabinet, felt for a mug, then poured himself some coffee.

"I'm so sorry for what I've done to the two of you," Vali said suddenly, her voice strained. "For dragging you into this . . . nightmare. You could have been killed today—and apparently because of me!"

Dan turned back to her. "It's not your fault, Vali. Can you think

133

of someone—anyone—who would have a reason to hurt you?"
He paused. "You say you didn't recognize this man?"

Vali shook her head. "No. When I first saw him at Cedar Point,
I thought he looked vaguely familiar. But later—No, I'm sure I've
never met him before."

"What are we going to do, Daniel?" Jennifer asked.

Dan took a sip of coffee, then set the mug on the counter. "I
think the first thing we'd better do is talk to the police. Vali, who
else knew we were going to Sandusky tonight?"

"Who else?" Vali hesitated, then replied slowly, "Well . . . Graham, of course." She paused. "And David," she added softly.

"No one else?" Dan pressed.

"No."

"What about Leda? Did you call her?"

"I tried. But I got her answering machine—she uses it through
the day when she's working. I left a message for her to call me
back if there was any reason we shouldn't drive in tonight."

"What time did you call?"

"Late this afternoon—three-thirty, maybe."

"Then Jennifer's tire had already been vandalized by the time
Leda could have known we were coming," he said, mostly to himself. He raked a hand down one side of his beard. "So . . . that
leaves Graham—who's in Columbus—and David. They're the
only ones who knew where we were going." Another thought
struck him, and he asked, "Did both of them know *why* we were
going to Leda's?"

Vali looked at him. "What?"

"Did you tell both David and Graham that we wanted to talk
with Leda about your dream?"

Vali was silent for a long time. "No," she finally said, her voice
uncertain. "I don't think I told either one of them. I *did* tell Graham everything else, though—about the headaches, the memory
flashes . . . everything. And David was here when I was on the

phone with Graham. I'm sure he heard the whole conversation. But no," she said again, "I'm almost positive I didn't say anything about Leda, except that we thought she might be able to help."

As Jennifer watched, Vali's expression changed from bewilderment to what looked like anger. "Graham was in Columbus," she said slowly. "So only David . . ."

Daniel put up a restraining hand. "Vali . . . I don't think we ought to jump to any conclusions. I *do* think it would be a good idea to call the police, though."

Vali got up and walked across the room toward the window. "I suppose you're right," she finally said in a soft voice, her back to them. "But if you don't mind, I'd like a little time. For one thing, I should call Leda and explain what happened. She'll be worried that we didn't show up. And I need to . . . get myself together."

Dan nodded and started to move toward the door, with Sunny at his heels. "Jennifer and I will go back to our place, get cleaned up a little, then come back over here, if you want."

Jennifer walked over and put her hand on Vali's shoulder. "Maybe you could rest for a little while, too. You look awfully tired, Vali."

"I . . . yes, I am," Vali admitted, still facing the window.

"Vali," Dan cautioned, "I don't think you should let anyone in—or talk with anyone—while you're here alone. No one but Leda. Until we know for sure what's going on."

Vali nodded, her head down.

Troubled, Jennifer watched her, then went to Dan, putting her hand on his arm. "We'll come back soon, Vali."

Finally, Vali turned away from the window. "Yes. All right. Thank you, Jennifer."

It was raining steadily when Jennifer and Daniel walked outside. Neither of them had a raincoat or jacket, so they jogged most of the way to the cottage. "Daniel, do you think it's David?"

"I don't know. The only thing I'm fairly sure of right now is that someone wants Vali out of the way." He stopped. "And it's beginning to look as if they've got the same thing in mind for us, too."

Jennifer shivered but said nothing. She glanced nervously around at the dark, deserted beach, then tightened her grip on Daniel's arm as they went on running.

NINETEEN

SOON after Daniel and Jennifer left, Vali called Leda, telling her only that they had had car trouble and wouldn't be coming in that evening after all. A few minutes later, she threw on a windbreaker and left the cottage. She suspected that the rain now falling steadily was merely the prelude to a hard storm. The lake was rolling with a gathering wind, and the night air seemed heavy and charged with electricity.

Indifferent to the wind and rain, she half-ran the distance from her cottage to David's house, guilt nagging at the back of her mind all the way. For her own protection, Daniel and Jennifer had asked her to talk with no one but Leda. If they had known she was going to see David, they would surely have tried to stop her.

Vali didn't know what accounted for the urgency to confront David alone, before the police—or anyone else—learned what was going on. Perhaps she wanted to discover the truth about his part in this nightmare before he could cover his tracks.

Or maybe she was secretly hoping he would produce an alibi, some proof of his innocence.

At any rate, she intended to face him before he had time to put up some sort of smoke screen. The possibility that David had been lying to her all along was almost more than she could believe. He had seemed so caring, so genuinely fond of her.

She had trusted him.

Tears spilled over and mixed with the rain pelting her face. She began to run even faster. There wasn't much time before Daniel and Jennifer returned to her cottage. She had to reach David first.

Vali deliberately ignored the fact that she might be placing herself in jeopardy by going to David's alone. Somehow, that didn't matter now. Besides, there was also a very real risk to Daniel and Jennifer. If David were the one responsible for all the treachery, confronting him alone might be the only way to protect her two new friends.

She raced up onto the porch to get out of the rain but stopped with her hand poised to knock when she heard music inside. It was David, of course. He was playing a Fauré nocturne, which surprised her; she had never thought of David playing anything but his own music. As she might have expected, he played it masterfully.

Vali had seen enough storms on the lake to sense that David's interpretation of the music was like the night itself—deceptively tranquil, but building to a brilliant storm of passionate, thundering force. Even as angry and hurt as she was, she found herself caught up in his artistry and command of the music. Only when silence fell did she finally manage to shake free of the compelling music and knock on the door.

The moment David appeared in the doorway Vali saw that he looked unusually tired and somewhat disheveled. His hair was tousled, his shirt not tucked in, and fine lines of fatigue bracketed his mouth.

Did she only imagine that his expression brightened when he saw her?

"What on earth are you doing out in this weather, Princess? Come inside and get out of the rain."

He reached as if to take her arm, but Vali brushed by him, avoiding both his touch and his gaze. She went to stand in the middle of the living room, near the piano.

"What's wrong, Vali?"

When he would have helped her out of her jacket, Vali threw it off, tossing it onto a nearby chair. Then she stood watching him, her hands clenched at her sides. "You look surprised to see me," she finally said.

He frowned, obviously puzzled by her behavior. "Surprised, but pleased. I have fresh coffee. Let me get you some."

"I don't want any coffee, David," Vali said tightly. "I want the truth."

He had turned to leave the room, but now stopped. "The truth?"

Vali swallowed down the knot of misery in her throat, suddenly aware that this was going to be even more difficult than she had thought. Physically and emotionally, she was stretched to the limit. Her head had begun to pound again, and she felt slightly ill.

David stepped a little closer. "Vali? Why don't you sit down, Princess? You look a little . . . shaky."

"I imagine I look considerably better than you expected, though, don't I, David?"

Again he frowned. "What are you talking about?"

"I think you know," Vali shot back, furious at his composure.

He shook his head. "Have I missed something?" He ventured a smile and reached for her hand. "Hey, Princess . . . I can see you're upset with me. But don't I at least get to know why?"

Vali recoiled from his touch, inching backward a few steps. "Why did you do it, David?"

"Do *what?*" He stared at her. "Look, I don't know what you're talking about, but I can't very well apologize unless you tell me what I've done."

Vali studied him in sick disbelief. "Oh, *stop* it, David!" she burst out. "Stop playing games with me."

His mouth tightened. *"What?"*

The thundering at the back of Vali's head intensified. For an instant she was afraid she was actually going to pass out. She pulled in a deep breath, trying to steady herself. "You should have thought your plan through a little more carefully, David. Oh, it probably would have worked if *I* had been driving. No doubt I would have panicked. But Jennifer's reflexes are much better than mine."

David closed the distance between them, grasping her by the shoulders. Anger sparked briefly in his eyes, then ebbed as he searched her face.

"You obviously think I know what you're talking about," he rasped. "But I swear to you, I don't. Vali—please, just tell me what's happened."

As limp as a rag doll under his hands, Vali was surprised to realize that she felt no fear. Only disillusionment. And a terrible sense of betrayal.

Betrayal. The thought acted like a trigger, exploding Paul's face onto the canvas of her mind. Paul's hands had also gripped her shoulders that night. His face, too, had been livid with anger. *Betrayal . . .*

Vali felt herself begin to sag. David caught her, led her across the room. She fought him, but he managed to ease her down onto the couch. His whisper-voice sounded distant, detached. She felt the blackness closing in, the pounding in her head racing faster and faster. She squeezed her temples between her hands with a soft moan.

"Vali . . . Princess . . . what is it? Are you ill?" When David coaxed her head onto his shoulder, Vali was too weak to protest.

She started to cry, silently berating herself for her weakness. Another wall of pain engulfed her, seizing her with such an excruciating agony that she gasped for relief.

"Vali, I'm going to get a doctor. Here, lean back. Lean back and close your eyes while I call a doctor."

"You tried to kill me . . . all of us . . . and now you're going to call a doctor?" Vali shot an incredulous look at him.

"*Kill* you—" David gaped at her, wide-eyed— "What in the name of heaven are you talking about?" He jumped to his feet, staring down at her.

For an instant, Vali wondered if she could have possibly been wrong. He looked so—stricken, so astonished at her accusation.

She pushed herself up off the couch, fighting the pain in her head, the crazy zigzags of color and shattered pictures racing before her eyes. "*Why,* David? What are you doing here? What do you want? What's so important to you that you'd try to kill three people?"

He shook his head slowly. "Vali—you've got to believe me. I haven't tried to kill anyone. I don't know what you're talking about, I tell you! I don't *understand!*"

Vali wished with all her heart she could believe him. Another thought struck her: She didn't *want* it to be David. He was too . . . important to her.

She looked away from him, trying to avoid his searching eyes. *Whether I want to believe it or not, he tried to kill me today. I mustn't forget that. I don't dare forget it.*

Without trying to touch her, David lifted both hands in a gesture of supplication. "Just . . . tell me," he whispered. "Tell me what it is I'm supposed to have done, Princess. Please."

Anger flooded Vali all over again. She took a step toward him, then stopped, struck by the thought that she was alone with this man, that he had tried unsuccessfully to kill her once, and that there was nothing to stop him from trying it again.

Why, then, didn't she feel threatened?

She heard her own voice as if coming out of a thick fog. "Did you know about the panel truck, David? Did you hire the driver? Or just the psychopath in the black sedan?"

She hurled words at him like stones, a furious, disjointed

account of the entire incident. She told him about the useless brakes, the slick highway, the black sedan and the driver. She told him everything she was sure he already knew. By the time she had finished her passionate recital she was drained, totally depleted of any strength she might have had.

"Vali . . . Princess . . ."

Suddenly she realized that David was holding her again, gripping her forearms, his gaze raking her face.

"Vali, did you say the brake lines were cut?"

Vali nodded, studying him with a dull, leaden stare. "You know they were," she said woodenly. "You know."

David winced, and she saw a small muscle by his left eye jerk spasmodically.

"You think I did that, Vali? Do you really think I'd do anything to hurt you?"

Vali tried to look away from him, but he wouldn't let her. He caught her chin with his hand and forced her to meet his gaze.

"Vali, listen to me. *Listen!*" he demanded when Vali tried to twist free. "It wasn't me, Vali. I would never do anything to hurt you. Don't you know that by now? I could never hurt you!"

How could he lie so convincingly, even now?

Vali felt tears splash down her face. She tried to free her hands, but David's grasp was unyielding. Before she realized what she was saying, the words tumbled from her lips. "Oh, David! Why— *why* did it have to be *you?*"

"Vali—" There was a new urgency in his whisper. "Please listen to me. Whose car was Jennifer driving—her own or yours?"

Vali gave him a blank look. "Whose car?" She hesitated. "Mine. She drove my car."

"Why? Why didn't she drive her own?"

Again Vali delayed her reply. "Her tire—someone put a nail in her tire."

His eyes narrowed. "Who else knew you were going to Sandusky tonight?"

Vali's throat was tight, her mouth dry. Her heart was racing as if it were about to explode out of her chest.

"It's important, Vali. Did anyone besides me—and Graham—know what you were planning to do tonight?"

She gave him an accusing look. "Just you," she choked out. "And Graham. No one else."

For a moment, David squeezed his eyes shut. Then he looked at her and said, "It wasn't me, Vali. I *swear* to you—it wasn't me."

Vali continued to watch him, wanting desperately to believe him. "Then . . . who?"

He pulled in a ragged, shallow breath. "Graham."

Vali tried to jerk free, but he held her. "No! Don't you *dare* blame him!"

David clutched her shoulders. "It was Graham." His steady, unwavering gaze held hers.

"Graham was in Columbus!" she spat out.

He shook his head. "No. He didn't go. Vali, you have to believe me. Graham is the one responsible."

Vali stared at him, her mind spinning.

David took her hand and again began to lead her toward the couch. His action broke Vali's paralysis. Seizing her chance, she yanked free of him and bolted for the door. But he outdistanced her, blocking her escape. "You can't, Vali! You're not safe anywhere but here now."

Vali choked off a sound of disgust and backed away from him.

"Vali . . . Princess . . ."

"Don't call me that!"

"I wouldn't hurt you."

"You tried to kill me. . . ."

"Never . . . I would never hurt you, Vali."

"You would have *killed* me. . . ."

"No! I love you, Angel. . . ."

Vali closed her eyes, then opened them. "What did you say?" she choked out.

"I love you," he said again, his whisper broken and hoarse. "I could never hurt you. You're my heart, my life."

Vali's mind spun out of control. "You're lying."

"Come here, Vali." He extended his hand.

Vali shook her head furiously.

He caught her hand, tugging her gently to him. Slowly, carefully, he drew her into the circle of his arms.

Vali felt the trembling of his body, heard him utter a deep, ragged sigh. "My love . . ." His lips brushed her brow with infinite tenderness. "It's true I'm not what you think."

Vali stiffened.

He tightened his embrace and pressed his lips against her temple. "Vali . . . Angel. . . . I'm not David Nathan Keye. I'm . . . Paul."

TWENTY

THE world stopped. Vali's legs buckled under her. She couldn't breathe, couldn't move, couldn't speak. She could only tremble in his arms, in the arms of this stranger, this madman who seemed intent on stealing her last shred of sanity.

His arms tightened around her, supporting her. "It's true, Vali."

He tipped up her chin, forcing her to look at him. Vali shook her head. "You're insane," she choked out.

"No."

Vali stared up at him in horror. "How dare you?" she whispered. *"How dare you!"*

He put her slightly away from him, clasping her shoulders only firmly enough to keep her from pulling free. His eyes burned into hers, trapping her in his gaze. "I can prove it, Vali. I know I don't look like myself. My face, my hair—everything is different. But not my heart. My heart is the same. It still belongs to you, Angel."

It was his use of the endearment again—*Paul's* endearment— that shattered what little control Vali had left. She cried out once, then again. He pulled her to him, holding her, soothing her, sheltering her in the hollow of his shoulder.

He urged her toward the couch. "Here, Angel, sit down," he whispered, touching his lips to her hair. "Sit here with me. I'm sorry. . . . I'm so sorry I did this to you. I know it's awful for you.

Here, sit close to me. . . . I'll tell you everything. . . . I'll tell you the truth, all of it."

Vali allowed him to pull her down beside him on the couch. He continued to hold her, gently but securely within his arms, stroking her hair. "I don't know where to start. There's so much . . . so much to tell you. . . ."

Tears streamed down Vali's face. Abruptly, she drew away from him as another thought struck her. "You're lying!" she said, her words spilling out in a breathless rush. "You can't be Paul. Your eyes—"

He held up an unsteady hand. "Wait," he said. He turned away for a moment. When he again faced her, he extended his hand, palm upward. He was holding two tinted contact lenses.

A stunned cry ripped from Vali's throat when she looked into his eyes—light gray, not dark. Pressing a fist against her mouth, she stared at him with a mixture of fear and disbelief.

He lifted a hand to gently smooth a wave of hair away from her temple. His touch was achingly tender when he brushed the tip of his index finger over her ear. "Little seashells," he whispered. "Remember? I always teased you that your ears looked like little seashells."

Vali shuddered on a choked, incredulous sob.

"Remember the day we spent at Radnor Lake?" His face softened to a smile that was both sad and reflective. "You took off your sandals so you could run free. But you sprained your ankle, and we ended up in the emergency room. Remember the nurse who admitted you? Her name was Sam. When she found out who we were, the only thing she was interested in was whether or not we knew Amy Grant." He threaded his fingers through her hair, then watched as if fascinated by the waves sifting through his fingers.

Tears began to spill from Vali's eyes again as she stared at him, remembering a man of incredible gentleness, a man whose love had always been sweet and steady and dependable. She squeezed her eyes shut, her shoulders heaving with the force of her silent weeping and tumultuous emotions.

He wrapped her more snugly in his arms. "Don't cry, Angel . . . don't cry anymore," he whispered against her lips. His kiss told her the truth as nothing else could have.

She dragged his name out of her heart as if it were the first time she had ever said it. *"Paul . . ."*

"Ah, what a feeling, hearing you say my name again, holding you again. . . ."

Vali reached up to touch his face, taking in every line, every plane of it as if seeking a familiar landmark. "Your eye," she choked out.

He closed his heavy left eye under her gentle touch. "The plane crash, Angel. My face was . . . destroyed. They had to give me a new one. A few weeks after the surgery, they noticed my eye was drooping a little. I told them to leave it. I wasn't about to start over."

She put her hand on his throat. "Your voice . . ."

"This is permanent, I'm afraid. My voice box was crushed."

"Your beautiful voice . . ."

Quickly he pressed his lips against the palm of her hand. "It doesn't matter. After everything else that's happened, it's not important. As long as I can still tell you I love you, that's enough."

Vali ran her hands over his shoulders. "You're so thin."

He shrugged and managed a wobbly grin. "Don't you remember? I don't eat when I don't work. And I wasn't able to work for months."

Choking on her tears, Vali examined his face with her hands much as Daniel Kaine had a few days before, slowly shaking her head in wonder. "But they said you were dead—the papers, the television—everyone told me you were dead!"

He grabbed her hands, framed them with his own, brushed his

lips over her knuckles. "You don't know how I hated that . . . but that's how it had to be." Suddenly he stopped. Looking up, he searched her eyes. "Angel, don't you remember anything about that last time we were together? The day I came to see you in Nashville, before I went to Washington? Anything at all?"

"Remember?" Vali shook her head. "No. Just . . . your coming to my apartment. You said you couldn't stay long, that you had to leave for Washington. You kissed me. . . ."

He nodded, a sad smile hovering about his mouth. "Nothing else?"

"No. I can't remember anything after that until . . ."

"The plane crash?"

"Yes," she whispered, then moved her hands to clutch his shoulders. "I wanted to die, too!" she cried.

"Oh, Angel, . . . I'm so sorry you had to go through that." His eyes misted as he studied her face.

Vali drew back from him, suddenly angry again. "How could you do that to me? How could you let me believe you were dead when you were alive? And for *three years!*"

A violent shaking racked her body. "Do you know what happened to me? I almost lost my mind! I was in a hospital for months; I was . . ." The words died in her throat.

He started to reach for her again, then let his hands drop away. "I know. . . . I *do* know, Vali. But there was nothing I could do. You see, while you were going through *your* nightmare, I was going through one of my own. Almost two years of plastic surgery, one operation after another—skin grafts, bone reconstruction, physical therapy. Then they started on the psychological conditioning. They turned me into a new person, gave me a whole new identity."

He reached for her hands, and Vali watched as he enfolded them in his. "What you have to understand, Angel, is that I *would* have been a dead man if I had come back into your life as Paul

Alexander. For months after the plane crash, I didn't know what they had told you. By the time I learned, everything had been set in motion, and there was no going back. They made it clear that my life—and quite probably yours—depended on my silence."

"They? Who are *they?*" Vali cried in frustration, yanking her hands away from him. "And carry *what* off? *Who* put you through the surgery? And where were you all that time . . . when I thought you were dead? I still don't understand how you could have let me believe I'd lost you, when you were alive the whole time!"

"It was the only way, Vali. You'll understand when I explain the whole story—"

"And when you finally *do* come back into my life, you don't look like yourself or talk like yourself or even *act* like yourself! You carry on this horrible . . . masquerade! You let me believe you're someone else, you lie to me—" Vali pressed the fingertips of both hands hard against her temples. *"Why?* Why didn't you just tell me the truth?"

He caught her shoulders and pulled her close, holding her gaze with his. "I couldn't. Telling you the truth would only have placed you in jeopardy along with me."

He continued to search her face as if he couldn't get enough of the sight of her. "Vali, after the plane crash, I was unconscious for days, then out of my head for weeks. I was totally irrational—delirious with pain. I was burned . . . horribly. Third degree burns over much of my body. You can't imagine the pain—"

He shook his head as if to banish the memory. "I, too, wanted to die. In fact, I *prayed* to die!"

Suddenly he seemed to realize the force of his grip and he released her. "All that time," he went on, "all that time they were rebuilding me, restoring me, pounding at me to make me realize that this was the only way I'd ever be able to come back into your life. If I were to . . . *live* again, it had to be as a new man. So I could come back to you and protect you from Graham. And, at the same time, help them get the evidence to stop him."

The impact of his words stunned Vali into silence. When she finally tried to speak, she felt as if her mouth had gone numb. *"Protect* me . . . from Graham? What do you mean?"

He studied her for a moment with a measuring gaze. "Vali, the plane crash that supposedly killed me was no accident. The engines were sabotaged. Graham . . . and the people he works for . . . were responsible."

Vali felt a cold shroud fall over her. She began to tremble. "Graham?" She shook her head in denial. "No. Graham wouldn't hurt anyone, especially not you! He loved you; he admired you; he wouldn't—"

"Graham is totally incapable of loving anyone or anything," Paul rasped, his eyes blazing. "Graham cares about nothing but his experiments, his work!" He got up and began pacing the floor.

Vali sat watching him, listening mutely as he told her about a conspiracy of terror too incredible, too fantastic, to be anything less than the truth. As he spoke, his words began to set into place the missing pieces of the puzzle that had held her memory at bay for years.

"The last day of my vacation that summer—the day before I was to come back to Nashville—I spent most of it with Mother, then went to see Graham." He paused. "This was while he was still at the Woodson laboratory, remember? Before he built the Center. It was late—eight, maybe nine o'clock—but it wasn't unusual for him to work that late. Since I planned to leave early the next morning, I decided to go over to the lab and tell him good-bye."

He stopped in front of her, reached in his shirt pocket for a stick of gum, and tucked it in his mouth.

"You never used to chew gum." The thought was totally

irrelevant. Vali didn't even realize she had spoken until Paul smiled at her.

"New habit for the new me," he said dryly.

"Anyway," he continued, "I started into the lab, but I heard voices, so I waited in the adjoining office. The door was ajar just enough for me to overhear the conversation taking place inside. What I heard froze my blood. I sat there and listened to my own brother commit treason."

"*Treason?*" Vali gaped at him.

Paul nodded. "Oh, I couldn't hear everything. But I heard enough to tell me that Graham had been concealing the results of some of his experiments from the Woodson people and selling— or trading—them to someone else. Someone," he said slowly and meaningfully, "not affiliated with our scientific community. The man who walked out of the lab with Graham that night had an accent that even *I* recognized as European."

"What kind of experiments?" Vali hugged her arms more tightly to her body, struggling to take in what Paul was telling her. "This sounds like something out of a science fiction novel."

Paul smiled grimly and dropped down beside her on the couch. "Doesn't it? That's what I thought, too, at the time."

He sighed and took one of her hands in his. "You may not know that Graham's specialty for years has been in the field of psychotropic drugs."

"Psychotropic drugs?" Vali repeated.

He nodded. "Drugs that affect the mental processes: marijuana, hashish, hallucinogens. But Graham has gone far beyond all those. He's developed some real state-of-the-art stuff—consciousness altering, memory blocking, redirection of thought patterns, and a lot more. He worked at top-secret level with Woodson for years to develop ideas for our own government, but Graham has always been too ambitious to remain just another research man."

He paused and for a moment sat studying Vali's hand, clasped in his. "What I heard that night at the lab made it obvious that Graham had a partner willing to finance his experiments in exchange for Graham's furnishing the partner's government copies of his research. For Graham, there would be a new laboratory, plenty of money—a scientist's dream." He looked at her. "The Alexander Center," he said, his tone bitter.

Vali looked at him, understanding now dawning quickly. "You said you were still there when Graham and the other man came out of the lab. . . ."

Paul nodded. "That was my first mistake."

"What do you mean?"

He uttered a short, voiceless laugh. "I've never been too good at keeping my mouth shut—I'm sure you remember—"

She glanced down at her lap, and for the first time since she had entered the house, she smiled, just a little. "Yes, I remember."

"I lit into Graham as soon as the other guy was out the door. I told him exactly what I thought of him and what I was going to do about it. Like a fool, I issued an ultimatum—told him to bring his entire obscene operation to a halt—or I would go to Uncle Kevin."

"Uncle Kevin?"

"Actually, he's one of my dad's best friends, but we've always called him 'Uncle Kevin.' He's been with the CIA for years. In the back of my mind, I suppose I thought I could either shame or scare Graham into cleaning up his act."

"Oh, Paul . . ."

He gave her a crooked grin. "I know—totally stupid. But I was *furious.* Not only because Graham was betraying his country but because of the kind of garbage he was fooling around with. I think all this mind-control stuff is immoral, Vali! And dangerous. Graham used to rant about the way scientists would eventually bring an end to all wars, that ultimately it would be the scientists who would establish universal peace—" He gave a small sound of disgust, running his hand through his hair.

"What did he say when you confronted him?"

"Oh, he was cool. Graham is *always* cool, you know. He looked at me with one of those cold-fish stares of his, then proceeded to explain how he had been doing some research for a private business in Europe. It was a slick comeback, but I knew him too well—well enough to know he was lying. Graham's an uncanny liar, but he's never been too successful at conning me."

He twisted his mouth with self-mockery. "Then I made my second mistake. I let him know I didn't believe anything he'd said and went charging out of the lab."

He stopped for a moment when a strong sweep of wind rattled the living-room windows, waiting until the noise from a sudden roll of thunder subsided before going on.

"I carried out my threat. I went to Nashville and called Kevin from a pay phone near your apartment. I told him what I knew, and he insisted I come to D.C. He even arranged for one of his people in Nashville to fly me to Washington on a private plane."

He leaned forward, propping his elbows on his knees and framing his face between his hands. "What I hadn't counted on was that one of Graham's pals followed me and found out about my trip to Washington. A few minutes from D.C., the plane's engine failed. The pilot managed to get a Mayday out on a scrambled frequency before we went down. An Agency helicopter picked up Kevin and arrived on the scene within minutes after the crash. The pilot was already dead. I was unconscious and badly burned."

He tapped the knee of his right leg. "My leg was caught under the seat, and they had trouble pulling me free. They got me out just in time. Kevin knew enough to suspect that the plane had been sabotaged. He and the helicopter pilot made an on-the-spot decision to report me as dead so Graham and his friends would think they had nothing to worry about. The plane was almost completely destroyed by fire." He shrugged, leaving the rest unsaid.

Vali's mind groped to make sense of what she had just learned. "They said there were . . . no remains. Nothing but ashes."

Paul grimaced. "It wasn't the first time the CIA falsified records."

"But how could they be so sure it was sabotage, that it wasn't an accident?"

Paul raised his head to look at her, and Vali saw the anger glinting in his eyes. "They weren't sure, not a hundred percent. Not until they got it on tape, thanks to a high-tech listening device that was installed in Graham's condo. Installed, incidentally," he told her with a thin smile, "by the same people who were buying Graham's experimental drugs and journals from him."

Vali frowned in surprise, and he nodded. "Right. His pals didn't trust him, either. They bugged his lab, his condominium—" He paused for an instant, then went on. "That turned out to work in our favor. One of Kevin's agents traced Graham's contact and found out where he's been staying. The agent spent over an hour in the guy's apartment the other night while this character and Graham were together at the Center. He copied some very interesting tapes—one of which includes a conversation about the airplane crash." He stopped, watching Vali carefully. "On one of the later tapes, there was a discussion about the most effective way to . . . take care of you."

Vali felt a sick knot of fear tighten in her stomach at the significance of his words.

"The main reason for *me* coming here," he continued, "was to keep an eye on you while the Agency did their job. They knew I wouldn't last a day if I came back as Paul Alexander. Not only could I incriminate Graham, but I could also identify his contact. Without an eyewitness, Graham probably wouldn't have been indicted. With my testimony, the charges are almost certain to stick."

"Oh, Paul," Vali exclaimed, "how can you testify against your own brother?"

"What choice do I have?" Paul shrugged, a frown creasing his brow. "What complicated things for me was finding out that you apparently remembered nothing about that day in Nashville, before I left for Washington."

At Vali's questioning frown, he tried to explain. "Vali, I told you everything that day. What I had learned about Graham—and what I was going to do about it. I told you where I was going— and why."

He rubbed his hands down over his face in a weary gesture, then looked up again. "When I first stopped by to see you, you were unhappy with me. I had already been gone for several days, and there I was about to leave again. I knew I shouldn't tell you what I'd learned, but you were so upset with me I went ahead and blurted out the whole story. Later, when I learned about your loss of memory, I was terrified to think about what might happen to you if you ever *did* remember. I'm sure Graham has considered you a threat all this time—just because there was always the chance you might know something, and he had no idea how *much* you knew."

Vali stared at him. "But why can't I remember . . ."

Suddenly she realized that she *had* been remembering. Pieces. Fragments. Scraps of memory had been floating in and out of her mind all day. She simply hadn't recognized them, hadn't been able to fit them together. Paul's face, his anger—that anger had been directed at Graham, she now realized, not at her.

Betrayal. He had spoken the word when he'd told her about Graham's deceit. And the bald-headed man—

"Did you describe Graham's . . . partner to me?" she asked abruptly. "Did you tell me what he looked like?"

Paul nodded, his gaze locking with hers. "Our man with the shiny dome," he said grimly.

"That's why he looked familiar. . . ." Vali said softly. "Oh, Paul—"

"Up until now," he broke in, "I thought the shock of the plane crash—and my 'death'—had somehow erased your memory. You know—a type of amnesia." His mouth thinned to a tight line. "But after overhearing your conversation with Graham today, I've got a hunch those little pills he's been giving you have something in them besides a tranquilizer."

Vali touched her fingers to her lips. "You think Graham deliberately—"

"Blocked your memory," he finished for her. "You bet I do."

Suddenly another thought sent Vali reeling. *"Leda!* She doesn't know? Leda doesn't know that you're . . . *alive?"*

He met her gaze. "No. And that's been tough. You know how sharp she is. I was really squirming the night of your birthday party."

At her questioning frown, he explained. "The strawberries, remember? She zeroed in on me with one of her eagle-eyed stares when I said I couldn't eat them. For a minute, I thought she suspected something." He gave Vali a rueful smile. "And when I sat down to play my piano again—" He shook his head. "I had been itching to get to it every time Mother had us over for an evening. Not being able to touch my own piano was almost as difficult as not being able to touch you." The expression of love and longing he turned on Vali brought tears to her eyes again.

"Oh, Paul! She's going to be so happy! Leda was devastated when she thought we'd lost you."

A look of regret crossed his face. "I'm a little worried about that. I'm afraid any joy she might feel at the sudden discovery that her . . . *dead* son is alive is going to be quenched by the realization that her *other* son is a traitor."

Vali leaned toward him. "Paul, that day in Nashville, did you say anything to me about Leda—something about not trusting anyone but her?"

He thought for a moment, then nodded. "Yes, I think I did. I was trying to protect you."

Vali felt almost dizzy with the realization that she hadn't simply imagined things, that the images that had been bombarding her throughout the day were, in fact, actual memories.

"Kevin told me I had placed myself in danger by shooting my mouth off to Graham," he went on. "He warned me to trust *no one*. I suppose I was trying to warn you of the same thing."

"It will be such an incredible shock to Leda," Vali said. "But your mother is so strong. She'll be all right."

Paul nodded, smiling a little.

"What are you going to do now?"

"Get us out of this mess just as quickly as possible," he said without hesitation. "I've already been pushing Kevin to wrap things up. He had hoped to wait until they could get some photos of Graham and his partner together. But after our trip to Cedar Point, I started getting really paranoid. I knew that incident with the carousel was no accident. And when Jennifer described the man she had seen . . ."

He expelled a long breath, rubbed the side of his right leg a moment, then went on. "The night your cottage was broken into—you thought I was in Nashville, remember? And I was. With Kevin. He met me there. I told him that, photos or no photos, I was going to tell you the truth by the weekend. He agreed and promised to take Graham and his cohort into custody by Saturday. Then I got back and found out what had happened at your cottage. . . ."

He shook his head. "When I heard you telling Graham today about the memory flashes, I knew I couldn't wait any longer. Kevin has warned me all along they would never let you remember—that they'd kill you first. I called him from a pay phone tonight, and he agreed not to delay any longer. My intention was to tell you the truth first thing tomorrow morning."

Determination lined his face. "But we're not waiting. I'm going to call Jeff and have him meet us at Mother's tonight. We'll be safe there until Kevin gets Graham and his pal on a plane."

Vali looked at him. "Jeff?"

Paul grinned at her. "Jeff Daly. The new man in Mother's life? He's an Agency man. You don't think the CIA would turn an amateur like me loose without backup, do you?"

"That's *terrible!* Leda is interested in Jeff—and she thinks he really cares for her!"

"And he does, Angel," Paul insisted, smiling. "He does. In fact, it seems that Jeff has developed such a fondness for Sandusky he's giving some serious thought to retiring there in the near future. Says it's time he was settling down."

Vali shook her head. It was too much to take in all at once. Life had suddenly become something wonderful and at the same time something terrible. She had never felt so overwhelmed, or so bewildered. For a moment she closed her eyes, as if by doing so she could somehow shut out all the ugliness, the pain, and the heartache of the last three years.

But then she remembered that her world *wasn't* ugly or painful any longer. Paul was alive. Paul was back.

She opened her eyes.

"Vali . . . can you forgive me?" Paul said, searching her gaze. He made no move to touch her, but instead pleaded with his eyes. "I honestly don't know what I would have done if I'd been conscious and capable of making decisions for myself. It was all taken out of my hands. You'll never know the guilt I felt when I finally learned what you must have gone through because of me. And you'll never know how desperately I've prayed that God would somehow carry you through the nightmare until we could be together again."

Vali lifted a hand and gently touched his face. He no longer looked like David Nathan Keye. This was Paul . . . her Paul.

"Vali, do you think you could still love me . . . as I am now? Could we start over again?"

Vali studied his face, love welling up in her. "Oh, Paul, we don't have to start over," she said softly. "I was already falling in love with *David,* but I was afraid to let myself care too much. Somehow I knew I felt as I did about David because he reminded me so much of *you.* Oh, Paul . . . I've never stopped loving you! Never!"

His face broke into the tender, adoring smile Vali remembered so well, and he reached for her. She went into his arms as if she had never been away.

She searched his eyes for the one familiar sign she had been looking for ever since he had first begun to tell her his incredible story. There it was, shining out just as brightly as she remembered. The look of love, so long restrained, had finally been set free.

"Welcome home, Paul," she whispered from her heart, just before he reclaimed her love with a long, cherishing kiss.

They shared one blissful moment of sweet reunion before a loud pounding on the door shattered the silence and startled them apart.

TWENTY-ONE

A N HOUR later, Jennifer and Daniel sat in the kitchen with Vali and Paul Alexander.

Jennifer could not stop staring at David. *Not David,* she reminded herself giddily. *Paul. Paul Alexander. In the flesh.*

She had been almost speechless with amazement from the moment the musician had opened his door and motioned them inside. After getting no answer at Vali's cottage, she and Daniel had arrived here, ready for battle. But their offense had been squelched by the sight of Vali, looking slightly dazed as she clung almost possessively to David's—*Paul's*—arm.

Vali had hurried to assure them that she was perfectly all right, then indicated that she—and *Paul*—had something to tell them.

Jennifer was still wide-eyed, her mind scrambling to take in the incredible story.

From across the table, Paul Alexander was smiling at her as if he knew what she was thinking. "Jennifer, why do I have the feeling you're sitting there trying to decide a fitting punishment for me?"

"Punishment?" Jennifer stared at him blankly.

"For misleading you," he explained.

After a moment's hesitation, Jennifer managed a rueful smile. "At least now I know why I never felt totally comfortable with you. It was so frustrating," she said bluntly, "liking you in spite of the fact that I didn't trust you."

"It clears up a couple of things for me, too," Dan added. "That first day we met, when I looked at you with my hands, I got a real surprise."

Paul nodded knowingly. "I got very nervous about that encounter. I had a hunch you might realize something wasn't quite right about my face."

"That's right, Daniel!" Jennifer blurted out. "I remember—you were surprised when I told you he was probably in his thirties. You thought he was younger."

"Thirty-two, as a matter of fact," Paul inserted with a grin.

"There's scar tissue around your hairline, isn't there?" Daniel asked. "From the surgeries?"

Paul's smile was a little forced. "Yes. I have a whole new face, Daniel. Not perfect—but new." He paused. "You said a couple of things bothered you. What else?"

"Your music," Dan replied.

Paul looked at him with a puzzled frown. "What? I worked for months, changing my style, even my notation."

"It was just a small thing," Dan explained. "You used to have a special little flourish when you modulated between keys that I'd never heard anyone but Paul Alexander use. I don't imagine that's easy to change."

"Apparently not, since I wasn't even aware I was doing it," Paul replied with a light laugh.

"What *I* want to know," Jennifer said, "is how you managed to . . . come back to life . . . and back into *Vali's* life as a musician."

Paul shrugged. "It wasn't that difficult, really. I was settled in a California condo for a few months, wrote some songs, waited for the Agency to use their contacts—and soon I was recording again. It didn't take long to establish a reputation on the Coast as a composer and an accompanist. From there, it was just a matter of getting a meeting with Vali's agent and a couple of producers."

"Where were you," Dan asked suddenly, "during your recovery and while they were getting you ready for your . . . reentry?"

"Different places," Paul said. "I was in a private—*very* private—clinic in Canada for the first year. Some of the later operations were done in Oregon. Later I was moved from one safe house to another until they settled me on the Coast."

Dan was quiet for only a moment before something else occurred to him. "The day you went to Nashville—," he said, leaning forward on his chair— "the day Vali's cottage was broken into . . . do you remember the talk we had that morning?"

"Most of it, I suppose. Why?"

"You went to a lot of trouble to fill me in on Vali's background and your own concern about her and Graham. At the time, I didn't understand why you were confiding so much personal information to someone you barely knew." He paused. "You were trying to put me on alert, weren't you? About Vali?"

Paul smiled at Dan's perception. "Exactly. I judged you to be a man who wouldn't be easily deceived, Daniel. And I sensed you were also a man willing to involve yourself in another's trouble. It was my own way of trying to provide a little extra protection for Vali."

When the whole story had been told, the four of them sat in silence for a long time. Once, Daniel shook his head as if still trying to assimilate the incredible tale of intrigue. Jennifer darted an occasional covert glance at Paul, only to find him looking at her with a knowing, slightly apologetic smile. Vali simply gazed at him as if she couldn't get enough of what Paul referred to as his "new face."

Daniel finally brought an end to the silence by pushing back his chair and getting to his feet. The retriever sleeping beside him also stirred and sat up. "I think I'd better take Sunny outside for a bit. It sounds as though the rain's let up for now," he said. "Want to come with me, Paul?"

The composer gave Vali's shoulder a light squeeze as he rose from his chair. "When we come back, I'll call Jeff. If he can meet us right away, we'll drive in to Mother's," he told her. Turning to Dan and Jennifer, he added, "I think both of you should come with us to Sandusky. I'm afraid you won't be safe until this is finished."

Jennifer waited, watching Dan's face. When he nodded his agreement, she sighed with relief.

"We probably shouldn't stay out here too long," Dan said as he and Paul walked along the shore. Freed of her harness, Sunny trotted ahead of them, occasionally turning and running back to check on her owner. "I think we're right in the center of the so-called calm before the storm."

"How can you tell?"

"Sunny," Dan explained. "She gets extremely hyper when there's an electrical storm on the way." He lifted his face, enjoying the spray off the lake, but still he felt edgy. "And so do I," he added.

"You're probably right," Paul said. "There are some pretty wicked-looking lightning flashes out there, and they seem to be getting closer."

They walked along in companionable silence for a while. At last Dan slowed his pace, saying, "All this must have been extremely difficult for you. Trying to hide your true identity from everyone—even your own mother. Your fear for Vali, trying to conceal your feelings for her. Frankly, I don't know how you carried it off so well."

"It was Vali who kept me going," Paul told him. "At first I was afraid Graham would try to get rid of her to insure her silence. I should have realized that manipulation is more his style. I think he was probably pressured into the idea of killing her. Not that he ever really cared about her," he added bitterly.

"Well, she should be all right now," Daniel said reassuringly.

"I hope so. But I'm worried about the drug he's been giving her, what sort of long-range effect it might have."

"I think she ought to see a specialist right away," Dan agreed.

"I wish you could have known Vali before this, Daniel," Paul said. "She was just beginning to bloom, just starting to develop a real sense of self-esteem. Up until then, she had always depended on other people—on *me,* at that time—for her identity. I tried to encourage her to be herself, to be the person God had made her to be."

They stopped walking. From the abrupt silence, Dan sensed that Paul had temporarily drifted back to the past. They stood quietly, indifferent to the light, drizzling rain. It was several minutes before they went on.

"I wish there were a way you could continue counseling Vali," said Paul. "She admires you a great deal, you know."

"Paul, you can do everything I could do for Vali—and more," Dan assured him. "You possess an unbeatable combination to help her: your love for the Lord and your love for her. It'll take a lot of prayer and a lot of patience, but my instincts tell me that any man who could survive what you have during the past three years has an abundant supply of both."

"Thank you, Daniel." Paul gripped his hand and shook it firmly. "Thank you for everything. Especially for caring enough to get involved—and on your honeymoon, yet."

Dan grinned. "I anticipate a lifelong honeymoon. We can spare a little time this week for friends." He turned and called Sunny back to him. "But for now, we'd better get back to the cottage. I don't think it's a good idea to leave Vali and Jennifer alone very long."

TWENTY-TWO

T HAT lightning is getting fierce," Jennifer said, glancing nervously out a window. "Do you think we should try to find an oil lamp or some candles—just in case?"

"I think there's a lamp out in the sunroom," Vali told her. "David says he likes to sit out there at night and—" She broke off with a shy smile. "I wonder how long it will take before I remember to call him Paul again."

Jennifer reached over and squeezed her hand. "Probably not long at all. But somehow I don't think he's going to mind very much *what* you call him—just as long as you continue to look at him with those stars in your eyes."

"None of this seems real to me yet," Vali said softly. Her expression sobered. "I don't suppose anything could spoil my happiness in having Paul back again, but I can't stop thinking about Graham. What he's done, what he *tried* to do."

"Vali . . ." Still clasping her hand, Jennifer searched for the right words. "Try not to think about Graham right now. You've been through so much today. There are a lot of things you'll have to face later. But for tonight, why don't you just . . . be grateful?"

Vali looked at her for a long moment, then said, "You're right. Paul will help me through the rest of it, when it's time."

"I think I'd better try to find that lamp now," Jennifer said, turning to leave the kitchen.

The sunroom was dark except for the erratic glare of lightning streaking through the glass-enclosed walls. Startled by the sight of the jalousie door standing open, she fumbled for the light switch on the wall as she entered the room.

She heard the step behind her a second too late. She felt a painful wrench in her shoulder as someone grabbed her arm and pinned it hard behind her back. At the same time, a rough hand covered her mouth, cutting off her scream.

Suddenly, only inches in front of her, a second man stepped out from the shadows.

Graham Alexander! A sudden bolt of lightning illuminated him in an eerie, spectral glow. He stood unmoving, his cold gray eyes appraising Jennifer with an impassive, almost clinical stare. He wore his usual tailored suit, so incongruous with his surroundings.

Cold fear snaked through Jennifer. There was something terrifying about the sight of Graham standing there like an ordinary businessman, watching her squirm under his gaze.

In her struggle to break away, she twisted sideways and caught a glimpse of the burly man holding her. The sight of his smooth-domed head and sinister features made her legs threaten to buckle.

"You won't need the light, Mrs. Kaine." Graham Alexander's quiet, frigid voice broke the silence.

Panic surged through Jennifer, propelling her to act. She kicked backward and, twisting, caught the man behind her off guard just long enough for her to break free.

But there was nowhere to run. Graham Alexander stood motionless directly in front of her. The other man was poised, ready to jump at her again. Jennifer felt like a trapped animal.

Graham lifted a restraining hand. "You've made all this much more difficult than it should have been, I'm afraid. If you and your meddling husband had minded your own business from the beginning, there would have been no need for anyone to get hurt."

Lightning flashed, illuminating him in incandescence. Jennifer's heart hammered once, then seemed to stop when her gaze met the cold, calculating stare of the scientist.

This man doesn't hate me, she thought suddenly, stunned by the unexpected insight. *He doesn't feel anything. He's empty. . . . He has an empty soul. . . .*

At that moment, she knew with a sickening flash of certainty that Graham Alexander was far more dangerous than any of them had suspected. The word *sociopath* darted through her mind, and she cringed inwardly at the terrifying suggestion that this was a man without feeling, without conscience.

"What are you going to do?" she choked out, trembling.

Graham shrugged, not answering. He blinked once, started to speak, then glanced beyond Jennifer's shoulder when he heard Vali's voice coming from the direction of the kitchen.

In desperation, Jennifer screamed out a warning. "Vali—get out! Get out of the house!"

"Shut up, you little fool!" Graham snarled and lunged toward Jennifer, his hand raised. At the same time, the other man pulled a handgun from his pocket and yanked her tightly against him with one beefy arm.

When Vali appeared in the doorway, Jennifer cried out to her again, but Graham had already moved to the door. He grabbed Vali, dragging her roughly into the sunroom and pushing her toward Jennifer, then stood scowling at both of them.

The bald man released Jennifer from his grasp, but remained so close she could smell the sweet, cloying scent of his aftershave.

"You—" He waved the gun at Jennifer. "Get over there by the wall. You, too," he ordered Vali, turning the gun on her.

They're going to kill us. . . . They're going to shoot us, and then they'll wait in here for Daniel and Paul . . . and they'll kill them, too. . . . They'll never have a chance. Jennifer began to pray silently, knowing with sick assurance that she was only moments away from death.

The man with the gun grunted a menacing obscenity when she hesitated, then shoved her so hard she fell against the wall with a thud. Dazed, Jennifer turned to check on Vali.

The singer was facing Graham. Her usually gentle, uncertain gaze was turned on him in incredulous anger.

"How can you do this?" Vali's voice shook violently. "What kind of a monster are you? First you try to kill your own brother, then—"

Graham's cold eyes suddenly narrowed. "What exactly are you talking about, Vali?"

She was trembling visibly. *"Stop* it! Don't you dare stand there and lie to me!"

Graham closed the distance between himself and Vali in two steps. For the first time, Jennifer saw a glint of feeling in his expression. It was rage.

"Spare me your simpering!" he snapped. "I asked you a question. What about Paul?"

Vali lifted her face and glared defiantly into his eyes. "The airplane crash, Graham—that's what I'm talking about," she spat out.

His anger seemed to flare once more, then ebb. In its place was an icy mask of contempt. "Poor Vali," he finally said in a tone that was chilling in its malice. "You really should have continued your medication, dear. In your case, memory is a definite liability." He sighed, then raised a hand to lightly trace the contour of the singer's lovely, stricken face. Jennifer saw Vali's eyes spark with a mixture of terror and revulsion.

"Such a waste, really," Graham continued. "I'd grown rather fond of you, you know. I even argued quite a strong case for your survival." He paused, staring at her for a moment. Then something seemed to snap shut in his eyes, and he smiled thinly. "Ah, well—you've been an enlightening experiment, at least. It hasn't been a total loss."

"That's all I've ever been to you, Graham? An experiment?"
Vali's voice held a tremor that hadn't been there before.

"Not entirely," Graham replied. "There was the matter of making sure you didn't know too much."

"About what you did to Paul."

He nodded. "Just out of curiosity, dear, what *do* you remember? Or perhaps I should ask you how much you knew to begin with? What exactly did my dear departed brother tell you?"

"Paul told me everything."

"Ah. I was afraid of that. That's why I had to start you on the medication right away. I saved your life, you know," he said with a deceptively guileless expression. "My partners were all for terminating you immediately, but I convinced them that your death coming so soon after Paul's might be a bit too . . . coincidental for some people. It seemed far more expedient at that point simply to keep you under observation."

"And now?" Vali's question was little more than a tremulous whisper.

"Now?" Graham fingered the collar of his white shirt as he stared at her. "I'm afraid you're no longer useful, dear. In fact, you've become a definite nuisance."

"So you're going to kill me." Vali uttered the words flatly, with no real evidence of fear. "Let Jennifer go, Graham. You can't possibly have any reason to hurt her or Daniel."

"You've only yourself to blame for what happens to the Kaines, Vali," he said reprovingly. "Had you not gone running to the blind man with your foolishness, they could simply have returned home in blissful ignorance. But now . . ." He let his voice drop off meaningfully.

"Graham, don't! Please."

He ignored her, turning instead toward his partner. "Get this over with. I'll go to the front and watch for the other two. Be ready to finish them when they come in the front door. We need to get out of here."

"*No!*" Vali lunged at him. "You nearly killed him once! You won't hurt him again!" Like a wild animal gone berserk, she hurled herself at the scientist, pounding at him and clawing at his face, sobbing as she struck out at him.

Graham's associate turned his gun on Vali, but Graham stopped him. "Wait!" he shouted. Grabbing both of Vali's hands, he held her captive. "What are you talking about? What's this about my 'almost killing' Paul?"

Suddenly Jennifer knew, with sickening certainty, what Vali was going to say. She tried to stop her, but it was too late. Vali flung the words out in a frenzy. "*He's alive, Graham!*" Vali watched his stunned look of bewilderment with apparent satisfaction. "You *failed!* Paul is alive!"

"You really *are* insane, you little fool!" Graham seized her by the shoulders and began to shake her.

"He's been right under your nose all along—"

Suddenly Vali gasped, pressed a fist to her mouth, and stared at him. Too late, she realized that she had placed Paul directly in the line of fire. She continued to stare at Graham Alexander, her face taut with fear.

He tightened his grasp on her shoulders, studying her in ominous silence. "Under my nose?"

Jennifer could almost see his mind working. His eyes glinted with suspicion, his face twisted to a menacing scowl. Suddenly his expression changed. "Keye," he said quietly.

Vali shook her head furiously. "No! No, I didn't mean it, I—"

Jennifer saw Graham's hand circle Vali's throat. "How long have you known?"

Vali's eyes went wild with terror, and she shook her head from side to side. "No, you're wrong. . . ."

Graham's face turned even uglier as he brought his other hand to her throat and began to squeeze.

Jennifer screamed—once in horrified denial, then again as a deafening peal of thunder rent the night and lightning struck a huge old cottonwood tree only a few feet from the sunroom.

Vali cried out, and both men turned just as the massive tree pulled free of its roots. Like a slow-motion sequence from a movie, it toppled directly toward them, its branches dragging a mass of power lines down with it.

Jennifer watched in horror as the entangled wires and tree branches struck the propane gas tanks directly outside the sunroom. Live electric wires sparked across the tank. There was a loud *whoosh,* followed by a blast. Flames shot up, and the glass wall at the end of the room exploded.

The bald man with the gun was closest to the explosion. Rocked by the blast and shards of flying glass, he collapsed at once. Graham Alexander lurched backward with the force of the blast, knocking Vali to the floor and pinning her under him as he fell.

Jennifer felt the sting of flying glass against her arms and forehead, and immediately dropped to the floor and covered her head. When the noise finally subsided, she lifted her head and looked around. Glass was everywhere. The entire far wall of the sunroom was in ruins, and fire was beginning to snake up the remains of the broken window frames. She could see the bald man, lying facedown in the rubble. Graham lay motionless on top of Vali's crumpled form.

With a cry of alarm, Jennifer scrambled across shards of broken glass to get to Vali. Still caught under Graham Alexander's unconscious body, the singer lay deathly still, a trickle of blood across her forehead.

"Vali! Vali!"

Vali's eyes fluttered open. "What happened?" she moaned.

"You're hurt—we've got to get out of here!"

With a valiant effort, Jennifer rolled Graham to one side and tried to pull Vali to her feet. Behind her, fingers of flame were already lapping at the garden chairs and tables at the other side of the room.

"Vali, come on! Can you walk?"

Vali's knees buckled, and she sank to the floor. "My ankle," she gasped. "It's—it's broken, I think."

Jennifer grabbed Vali under the arms and began to drag her across the floor. The room was filling up with thick, heavy smoke. Her eyes watered, and her throat burned. "We don't have much time," she coughed.

Vali shook her head. "Graham's still alive. We can't leave him here!"

Against Vali's protests, Jennifer staggered toward the kitchen, dragging Vali along with her. "The smoke won't be as bad in the kitchen," she shouted.

"Don't leave him, Jennifer! Please!"

By the time they reached the doorway, the kitchen had also begun to fill with smoke. "I can't breathe," Vali choked out, wheezing. "Leave me . . . get Graham."

Exhausted, Jennifer laid Vali down on the kitchen floor. "He tried to kill you!" she protested.

"He meant . . . something to me. And he's Paul's brother." Vali tried to take a breath but was gripped by a wracking cough.

Jennifer shook her head. "I don't have the strength to carry him out."

"Get help." Vali gripped Jennifer's arm with surprising power. *"Please!"* Then her head sagged to one side, and her eyes closed.

Jennifer looked through the doorway into what was left of the sunroom. Flames were beginning to lick up the walls, and smoke was pouring out. Vali was pale and clammy, her breathing shallow—probably in shock. She had no choice. If she stayed here with Vali, they would both die.

Frantic, she scrambled to her feet and tried to stand. Her legs would barely hold her. Gripping the kitchen counter for support, she made her way through the living room to the door, flung it open, and staggered out onto the porch.

⚞⚟

Dan and Paul heard the explosion when it hit. With his hand in a death grip on Sunny's harness, Dan began to run as fast as he could toward the house. He could hear Paul's labored breathing behind him.

He pivoted toward the sound. "Are you all right?" he yelled.

"My leg—I can't keep up," Paul rasped. "Can you make it without me?"

"I've got to get to the house—"

"Go on! I'll be right behind you!"

Dan kept going, with Sunny beside him. Once he tripped in a hole and nearly fell, but he scrambled to his feet, fumbled for Sunny's harness, and kept going. His senses filled with the sound of the storm and the scent of smoke.

"Daniel!" Jennifer's frantic voice reached him above the wind and thunder. *"Daniel!"*

"I'm here, Jennifer!" With relief, he felt her hand on his arm.

"Daniel, where's Paul? Vali needs help!"

"He's right behind me—or should be. What about Vali?"

"She's inside. Daniel, the fire . . . Graham . . . we've got to get them out!"

Dan gripped her arm firmly. "Slow down. What about Vali and Graham? Where are they?"

"Vali's in the kitchen. She broke her ankle, I think. And she's swallowed a lot of smoke. She passed out—I'm pretty sure she's in shock. Graham's in the sunroom, but—"

Paul limped up behind them, panting heavily. Daniel turned toward the sound of his gasping breath. "Vali's inside. Let's go!"

When they got to the front door, Daniel turned to Jennifer. "Take Sunny. Go to a neighbor's and call the fire department—and an ambulance. Paul and I will go in."

"Daniel, I'm not leaving you here."

"We'll be OK. Paul will be my eyes. Now, go!"

Dan listened to Jennifer hurry off with Sunny in tow, then turned to Paul. "Can you do this?"

"I'll be all right," Paul rasped.

But Daniel heard the slight hesitation in Paul's reply. *Of course,* he remembered. *The plane crash . . . the fire . . .*

Daniel reached for him. "I know this is tough, after all you've been through. But we'll make it. We *have* to." He groped for the doorknob and flung open the door. He could feel the heat, smell the smoke. "You go first—on all fours. I'll grab your ankle and follow you. Don't go too fast—and don't stand up."

He heard Paul drop to his knees. "Ready, Daniel?"

"Ready."

They started to crawl slowly through the living room. The smoke was thick and heavy. "It's so hard to see," Paul muttered.

"Can you see the flames?"

"Not yet," Paul rasped. "But the smoke is—" The rest of his sentence dissolved in a fit of coughing.

"How much further?"

"We're almost . . . to the . . . kitchen."

Dan could feel the effects of the smoke in his lungs. His chest felt as if it could explode, and his eyes burned and watered.

"I see her!" Paul's raspy whisper reached his ears.

"How much further?"

"Only a foot or two. Vali!"

They reached her, and Dan groped to feel her pulse. She was

176

unconscious, but her pulse was fairly strong. "We have to get her out of here!"

Paul didn't answer.

"Paul?" Dan repeated. "Are you all right?"

"I'm here." The raspy voice began to cough. "The fire's moving this way. Part of the wall is gone."

"Then let's go!"

"I *can't.*"

Dan's lungs felt as if they would burst. He tried to get a breath and began to wheeze against the smoke. "We don't have much time!"

"I've got to go after Graham," Paul's whispery voice said. "Can you take care of Vali?"

"I think so, but—"

Paul squeezed Dan's shoulder. "I have to do this. I . . . I know what it's like to burn—to nearly die in a fire. Nobody deserves that—not even Graham."

Dan was acutely aware that their time was limited. In spite of the rain, the blaze was sweeping through the house and might be upon them at any minute. But he heard the plea in Paul's desperate whisper, and he couldn't bring himself to argue. "He's in the sunroom, Jennifer said. Can you get that far?"

"I'm going to try. Just get Vali out. *Please.*"

Then he was gone, and Dan was alone. A sense of hopelessness swept over him, but he fought against it. For once, his sightlessness was more of an advantage than a burden. He didn't need to see in order to crawl, and he didn't have to see to pull Vali's limp body through the room. All he had to do was go out the way they had come in. And keep praying as he went.

When you pass through the waters, I will be with you; and through the rivers, they will not overflow you. When you walk through the fire, you will not be scorched, nor will the flame burn you. . . .

The enormous lung capacity Dan had developed during his

years of training as an Olympic swimmer served him well. He could hold his breath for an incredibly long time, even under physical exertion, and he now used that ability to keep from being overcome with smoke.

He shall cover you with his feathers, and under his wings shall you trust. . . .

He felt a little more secure when he reached the edge of the living room carpet. But then he felt Vali begin to move, to thrash against him as he dragged her forward.

"Vali? It's me, Daniel. Don't struggle. Just stay with me, OK? We're almost out."

Dan heard her gasp, then begin to choke. When her coughing had subsided, he began to inch forward again, dragging her with him.

"Dear Lord," Daniel muttered, staggering forward. "Help us!"

The Lord will guard your going out and your coming in from this time forth and forever. . . .

At that moment he felt a touch of damp night air from the open front door.

"Oh, Daniel—"

"Jennifer?"

"I'm right here, Daniel! I'll take Vali now."

He felt her brush past him. "She's alive, Daniel. She's all right."

Exerting the last ounce of his energy, Dan stumbled out onto the porch. From a distance so far away that it seemed to be coming from another world, another time, he heard the urgent wail of approaching fire engines. Then voices. Someone helped him off the porch and set him down in the wet grass on the far side of the yard. He felt a hard shove from a furry body and smelled the musky scent of wet dog as Sunny nuzzled against him and licked his face.

The fire had not harmed their bodies, nor was a hair of their heads singed. . . .

TWENTY-THREE

PAUL Alexander knelt on the grass behind the house. All around him, he could hear sirens wailing and voices shouting, but none of it mattered to him. He was aware only of the burned and dying form of the man who lay in front of him.

Graham. His twin brother. His brother who had betrayed him, had tried to kill him.

But still . . . his brother.

Now they were truly twins. Graham had been burned, severely burned, just as he himself had been in the plane crash. Graham had felt the same pain, the mind-destroying, crushing pain of fire. He was alive, but just barely.

"Graham," Paul whispered. "The medics are on the way."

The eyes flickered open, wild and stark against the blackened face. "Too late . . ." he rasped.

Paul knew he was right, yet his heart wrenched at the reality of his brother's impending death. Graham shuddered, and Paul felt his pain.

He remembered. He remembered the agony, the terror, the devastating sense of helplessness. He knew what his brother was going through, and in a way, he was going through it with him.

As he stared down at the disfigured, ravaged body, Paul felt no anger. Only pity. Pity and an overwhelming sense of despair and loss. It shouldn't have been this way. They were brothers. How had it come to this?

Graham's breath rattled in his throat. He gasped for air. His head lolled to one side, and the life left his body.

"God, be merciful to him," Paul whispered. "God, be merciful to us all."

Then with infinite tenderness he reached to close his brother's eyes.

***

Sprawled outside on the lawn, as weak as he had ever been in his life, Daniel lay resting, enjoying the feel of Jennifer's arms around him, her murmurs of wifely concern.

"Are you sure you're all right, Daniel?"

"I'm fine. But Vali—"

"Vali is already on the way to the hospital. The medics said her ankle was broken, and she took in an awful lot of smoke. But she'll be all right."

"Paul—"

"Paul followed the ambulance to the hospital. He'll stay with Vali."

She said nothing for a moment, then started in on him again. "Daniel, are you absolutely positive that you're all right?"

He smiled. "Don't I look all right?"

"You look beautiful," Jennifer assured him between sobs. "Your face is black and your eyes are all red and your clothes are ruined. But you look beautiful, Daniel!" She hugged him to her as if to confirm her own words, smothering his face with kisses.

"We're quite a team, aren't we?" said Daniel.

"We're a *great* team!" Jennifer agreed.

Dan thought for a moment. "One thing, though," he said.

"Yes, Daniel?" She was still sobbing.

"Now that I've seen your idea of a honeymoon—" He paused as she kissed him again. "Would you mind very much if I handle our vacation plans in the future?"

EPILOGUE
November

"I still can't believe we're here, Daniel. This has to be one of the most exciting things that's ever happened to me!"

"Thanks," Daniel said dryly. "Where are our seats?"

"Orchestra section," Jennifer said distractedly, her head swiveling back and forth to watch the crowd pouring into The Performing Arts Center.

"Mm. First class. Do you see Leda anywhere?"

"No. I can't see much of anything from here."

A red-haired man wearing a sport coat and sweater vest approached them, smiling. "Mr. and Mrs. Kaine? I'm Grandy Hayden—Paul's manager. He asked me to meet you." He shook hands with Dan and Jennifer, glancing with interest at Sunny, who stood patiently at Dan's side.

"Your seats are down front. Paul's mother is already there. I'll take you to her, if you like."

He stepped in front of them and started walking. "Have you been at TPAC before?"

"No, we haven't," Jennifer replied. "We've been in Nashville, but this is our first time at the Center."

"Looks like most of Nashville is here tonight," Hayden said, glancing around. "I think we're going to have people hanging from the ceiling before long." He stopped to let someone pass, then went on. "Paul says the two of you are providing the music for the wedding tomorrow."

Jennifer nodded energetically, trying to ignore the butterflies in her stomach.

The concert hall was enormous, and already every inch of available space, both downstairs and in the tiered balcony, was packed.

As they neared the front, Jennifer spotted Leda, who stood when she saw them and waved. She embraced them warmly when they reached their seats, and Jeff Daly, at her side, stood and shook hands. Leda then introduced Vali's Aunt Mary, who was sitting on the other side of Jeff. Grandy Hayden waited until they were settled in their seats, then left to go backstage.

Leda continued to squeeze Jennifer's hand. "I think I'm more excited than the kids tonight!" she said. "Isn't this an event, though? The two of them together on a stage again for the first time in over three years?" She glanced toward the stage, then back at Jennifer. "So—are you ready for this big weekend? I'm already exhausted! And Vali—" She rolled her eyes heavenward. "I don't think that child has slept for a week. I told her she's going to collapse before the wedding tomorrow if she doesn't get some rest, but she doesn't hear me—she's too busy!"

Dan grinned at her. "How's Paul doing? Is he nervous?"

Leda arched one dark brow in amusement. "About the concert? No. He doesn't get too tense about performing. But the wedding?" She shook her head and threw up both hands. "He's hopeless."

As if by mutual consent, no one mentioned Graham. Jennifer knew it had to have been a shattering experience for Leda to have one son returned to her while losing the other to a horrible death.

According to recent newspaper accounts, Graham Alexander's research company was under investigation. The CIA had discovered ample documentation of treason. Graham's cohorts would be behind bars for years.

With a meaningful glance at Jeff Daly, Jennifer lowered her

voice to a conspiratorial whisper. "Is it possible there's going to be another wedding in the near future, Leda?"

"It's under discussion," she answered slyly. "But I think we'll elope. I'd never muster the energy to survive two big—"

The sudden dimming of the lights, followed by a crashing, reverberating cadence of synthesized chords, made her stop and turn toward the stage.

Jennifer clutched Dan's hand in anticipation as the music continued to echo from a darkened stage. The waiting crowd began to cheer, already recognizing the unique sound of Paul Alexander's music.

A spotlight isolated Grandy Hayden as he hurried onstage, and the music ebbed to a soft backdrop when he started to speak. He grinned and waited to make himself heard.

"I won't draw this out—" The crowd applauded. "You've waited long enough. Besides, there's probably nothing I could tell you that you don't already know. By now you've heard their story. You know where they've been and what they've gone through." His expression sobered and he paused a beat before going on. "Three years ago, you thought you had told them good-bye." His smile returned. "Now, say hello . . . to Vali Tremayne and Paul Alexander! By the grace of God—together again!"

He made a sweeping gesture with one hand, backing off the stage as the lights went up and the music thundered. The crowd rose to their feet in unison, exploding into a deafening roar of cheering applause.

"Tell me *everything*," Daniel said in a voice loud enough to be heard above the crowd and the music.

"There's Paul! Oh—Daniel—there he is!" Jennifer cried, clutching eagerly at Dan's arm. "He's at his keyboard! Oh, my goodness, he looks so different! He's gained weight. And his hair is darker again . . . it still has lots of silver, though . . . and he still has a beard. He looks *wonderful!* He looks *happy!* And he's still chewing gum, bless his heart!"

The din in the hall increased to a roar as Paul and his group moved into the familiar hit song associated with Vali throughout her meteoric career. Even lovelier than Jennifer remembered, she ran onto the stage wearing white silk, her magnificent hair blazing about her head. She faced the people once, opening her arms wide in welcome, then crossed to Paul and took him by the hand.

The two of them came center-front, their faces beaming with love for the crowd and for each other. Twice Vali had to wipe the tears from her eyes. Once she was overcome and pressed her head against Paul's shoulder for a moment until she regained her composure.

Leda was crying openly. It seemed to Jennifer that everyone in the hall was crying, and she was no exception. Even Daniel was dabbing at his eyes with his handkerchief.

It took almost ten minutes before the crowd settled down, and even then Paul had to call for order. Taking a microphone, his eyes twinkled with mirth as he looked out into the audience. "For those of you who were expecting David Nathan Keye, I apologize for the last-minute switch."

After their laughter subsided, he grinned at them and asked, "Well—you want to stand here and cry all night, or do you want some music?"

The uproar made it clear they wanted music. And they got music—a wide variety. The well-loved and familiar numbers Vali and Paul had made popular years before—the golden oldies, as Paul referred to them—plus a wealth of new numbers Paul had turned out since moving back to Nashville. There were hand-clapping, joyful praise songs, melodic ballads like *Vali's Song,* gospel songs and hymns and Scripture songs. Years of treasured Christian music were poured out as a love offering to the Lord in the presence of his people.

"Vali seems so much more confident," Jennifer remarked to Dan once, noting the pleased smile her words brought to his face. "She's just dynamite up there!"

"We're in the presence of greatness, darlin'," said Daniel.

"They're so *good* together!"

"Like us," he said with a sage nod.

"Like us," Jennifer repeated, checking his expression for any hint of levity but finding none.

Returning her attention to the stage, she saw Paul grab a microphone and drape his other arm around Vali. He looked exhausted but happy as he began to address the crowd.

"We really have to quit sometime tonight, people," he said, meeting the chorus of protests from the audience with an upraised hand and a grin. "Wait . . . wait a minute . . . just in case there's anyone out there who doesn't know this by now, I have something to tell you."

He brought the mike a little closer to his mouth and leaned forward to the audience, his eyes sparkling with mischief. His teasing grin broke into a broad smile of unrestrained joy with his dramatic announcement. "We're . . . getting . . . married . . . tomorrow!"

He turned to a blushing Vali and kissed her soundly, with loud and energetic approval from the audience.

Paul waited until the din subsided, then spoke again into the microphone, slowly and distinctly so his whisper-voice could be understood.

"Tonight is a special time of reunion for Vali and me. Our being together again is a miracle for which we'll never cease to thank God. We're grateful beyond words to be able to stand up here together and look out and see the people we love. Among those people are two very special friends the Lord brought into our lives at a time when we needed them most."

Paul smiled out at them and continued. "Most of you have

probably heard of one member of this marvelous duo. A few months ago, a musical by the title of *Daybreak* swept the Christian community. Not only has the musical itself changed numerous lives, but the title song has become an anthem of hope for Christians throughout the country. It will be a part of our wedding service tomorrow, but we wanted to share it with you tonight. *Daybreak* was written by a great man named Daniel Kaine. We'd like for you to meet him and his beautiful wife, Jennifer, . . . right now."

The next thing Jennifer knew, Paul had bolted from the stage, slowed very little by his stiff leg, and was headed toward her and Daniel. The crowd broke into pleased applause as they embraced, then linked arms. Paul coaxed them up to the stage, where they were welcomed by a misty-eyed Vali. She gave each of them—including Sunny—a fervent hug.

After leading Dan to the grand piano, Paul returned to his keyboard. A hush fell over the entire auditorium. Dan hesitated only a moment before sounding the opening chords of *Daybreak*. Paul waited a few measures, then added the electronic equivalent of a full orchestra, and the two of them began to offer a sacrifice of praise that Jennifer felt sure had the angels in heaven singing with them. Finally she and Vali, coming to stand behind Dan at the piano, added their voices to the music.

There was not a dry eye in the auditorium or a single person remaining in his seat as the four on stage repeated the *Daybreak* finale. They built in volume as they built the emotion, giving their voices, their hearts, and their spirits over to the music that God had used time after time, first for Daniel . . . and now for others.

Standing behind her husband, Jennifer watched the mastery and the consummate skill of his hands at the piano. As he played, she felt the power in his massive shoulders and the power in his spirit. Then a sudden flash of insight shook her to the very core of her being.

She looked up from Daniel and out into the mass of people whose voices were raised in one thundering hymn of communal praise and saw, not a sea of strangers, but a family of loved ones. In that moment, she caught a glimpse of what the Lord had desired for his children from the beginning of creation . . . a oneness, a unity of heart and spirit and purpose with the power to transcend individual needs, bridge nations, unite governments, and join worlds as a body fitted together and secured in place by the love of Jesus Christ.

After the last chord had sounded, Daniel stood, and Paul came to join them. The four linked hands and walked to the front of the stage, basking in the unity and the love that filled the hall.

As the cheering continued across the immense, overflowing auditorium, Jennifer glanced from Vali to Paul, then to the audience, and finally to her husband.

"What are you thinking, Daniel?" she asked, close to his ear in order to be heard.

He hugged her tightly and gave her a smile that went straight to her heart. "I was thinking," he said quietly, "how much the Father must enjoy these family reunions."